CW00539217
Meal-plan
your way to
weight loss

Meal-plan your way to weight loss

Advice and recipes from top WW Coaches Rebecca Burnicle and Wendy Van Staden

Contents

Welcome to WeightWatchers 6

The WW PersonalPoints™ program 8

Track your recipes 9

Non-starchy vegetables 10

WW meal-prepping for success 12

How to get the most out of your freezer 16

Our smart swaps 18

Meet your Coaches 20

Rebecca's story 22

Why and how I prep 26

Rebecca's meal-prep hacks 28

Rebecca's weekly meal plan 30

Rebecca's grocery list 32

Wendy's story 34

Why and how I prep 38

Wendy's meal-prep hacks 40

Wendy's weekly meal plan 42

Wendy's grocery list 44

Recipes 46

Breakfast 48

Lunch 74

Dinner 102

Snacks 162

Dessert 198

Acknowledgements 230

Conversion chart 234

Index 235

Welcome to WeightWatchers

From humble beginnings to the world's leading sustainable weight-loss program with over 5 million members, WeightWatchers has come a long way since it all started more than 59 years ago, evolving from one woman's inspiring success story to that of many.

WHERE IT ALL BEGAN

Jean Nidetch, the company founder, had been overweight most of her life. She had become discouraged by years of fad dieting, having tried pills, hypnosis and numerous quick-fix approaches, all of which led to regained weight. She decided to seek medically backed guidance instead, and entered a free 10-week weight-loss program called the 'Prudent Diet', sponsored by the New York City Board of Health's obesity clinic. She lost 9 kg, but her motivation waned with the lack of peer support she had received during the program. This is when Jean's weekly meetings with her own support group began, and the seed for WeightWatchers was planted.

Jean began her own weight-loss support group by inviting some of her friends to her home once a week to discuss their goals, tips and challenges for weight-loss success. As word spread and attendee numbers grew, she finally launched Weight Watchers Inc. in May 1963. The first official meeting, held in a rented loft above a movie theatre in Queens, New York, attracted more than 400 attendees. The winning formula of WeightWatchers quickly spread across the world and to Australia in 1969, where the first meeting was held in Sydney.

WHAT WE DO TODAY

We are a human-centric company powered by the world's leading sustainable weight-loss program. Having constantly evolved in line with the latest science and member needs, we've stood the test of time, delivering a trusted program that remains a category leader both in Australia and across the globe. WeightWatchers has retained the number-one spot for weight loss for 12 consecutive years, as judged by an independent panel of experts in the U.S. News & World Report. It's also backed by more than 100 clinical studies and is supported by even more incredible member success stories.

At WW, our purpose is to inspire healthy habits for real life. While supporting members at physical locations and virtual Workshops, we have also built a digital experience centred on the award-winning WW app that allows people to learn healthy habits their way. In addition to food, fitness, sleep and water tracking, the WW app includes everything from recipes and 24/7 WW Coach support, to a barcode scanner, meditations, and audio and video workouts, providing support across the pillars of food, activity, mindset and sleep.

COMMUNITY AT OUR CORE

Community remains at the heart of our philosophy and it is this community that differentiates us in the market. Our network of Coaches, Ambassadors and members live our purpose daily, encouraging and supporting each other through our community platforms to pay forward the techniques and success they've achieved with others. We are incredibly proud of our members' achievements and even more so of their ability to make these changes lasting and sustainable.

What's that symbol?

Our guide to finding the best recipes for your dietary needs

Gluten free

Recipes with this symbol either don't contain any gluten or a gluten-free substitute is available. Check the ingredients list of all packaged food to be sure and take care with cross-contamination.

Dairy free

Recipes with this symbol are free from all dairy products or use a dairy-free substitute.

Vegetarian

Recipes with this symbol don't contain meat or fish, but may have dairy products or eggs.

Vegan

Recipes with this symbol don't contain any animal products, including meat, dairy, eggs and other animal-derived substances.

Nut free

Recipes with this symbol don't contain any nuts or nut-based products. Check the ingredients list of all packaged food to be sure and take care with cross-contamination.

Freezer friendly

Recipes with this symbol can be kept in the freezer for a period of time. Check recipes for freezing, thawing and reheating instructions.

Adds PersonalPoints™

Spot this symbol under a recipe? It means that the recipe contains at least 1 serving of non-starchy veggies, which may contribute to adding Points to your daily Budget. When you track the recipe in the WW app, any extra PersonalPoints™ will automatically be added to your Budget.

Please note: the recipes in this book have been reviewed by our team of qualified nutritionists to ensure that the information listed is as accurate as possible. However, people with food allergies or sensitivities should always check the ingredient information of the products they consume to ensure that they meet their dietary needs. Recipes have been tested in a fan-forced oven; if you are using a conventional oven, we recommend adding 20°C to the recommended temperature.

Cooking measurements in this book have been presented in line with the Australian metric system. For New Zealand customers, we recommend weighing or measuring out tablespoon measures as per the grams or ml provided in the ingredients lists, as the tablespoon size is larger in Australia.

The WW PersonalPoints™ program

Everything you love is on the menu. Yes, everything!

That's because we use the latest in nutritional and behavioural science to help make losing weight – and keeping it off – simpler. It's your journey and you're in the driver's seat, so you can live your fullest life, no restrictions and no deprivation, while still losing weight. There's truly no food that's off-limits.

Our latest WW program delivers a truly flexible, individualised path to sustainable weight loss for every member.

HOW?

Now more than ever, PersonalPoints will nudge you towards healthier foods. We've updated our algorithm using the latest nutrition science, factoring in even more nutritional elements to guide you towards foods higher in healthy fats, fibre and protein, and lower in added sugars and saturated fats.

Based on what you tell us you love to eat, our nutrition experts craft a list of ZeroPoint foods and a PersonalPoints Budget that's unique to you, your goals and what you like to eat. No two plans are alike – which means it fits into your life, so you don't need to conform to it.

Your PersonalPoints Budget is just the starting place. For the first time ever, you can earn PersonalPoints for doing healthy habits like drinking water, eating non-starchy vegetables and staying active, so that it feels like second nature – not work. The best part? You never have to worry about running out of PersonalPoints or going hungry!

*

PersonalPoints™ are included for each recipe

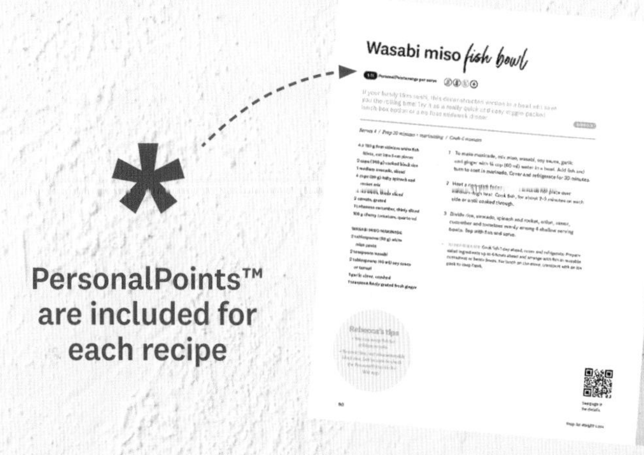

Wasabi miso *fish bowl*

Track your recipes

To make tracking easier than ever for our WW members, we've added a QR code to each recipe for quick, seamless tracking in the WW app. Simply open your camera on your smartphone and hover your device over the QR code.

Research shows tracking your food can not only help you lose weight, but can support weight maintenance too. This is because tracking makes you more aware of what you're eating and how much you're eating, and can help guide you towards healthier choices. Whether you track as you go, or track at the end of each day, there's no one-size-fits-all approach to tracking. The most important thing is finding a way that best suits you, and one that you'll be most consistent with in the long term.

For non-WW members

The recipes in this book are all WW approved. They can be used and enjoyed without the app.

Interested in joining WW? Learn more about our program at ww.com/au. Scan this QR code to receive your special offer.

Non-starchy vegetables

'Zero' usually means 'nothing'. But at WW, ZeroPoint™ foods are everything! While plans are customised to each member, there's one universal category of ZeroPoint foods that everyone has: non-starchy veggies. These are filled with tonnes of nutrients – potassium, vitamin C, and specifically fibre, which helps you stay fuller, longer. For every 1 serve (1 cup) of non-starchy vegetables that you eat on the WW Program, 1 PersonalPoint will be added to your daily Budget.

NON-STARCHY VEG LIST

Raw, cooked, fresh, frozen or canned (without added oil or sugar)

* Alfalfa sprouts
* Artichokes
* Asparagus
* Baby corn
* Bamboo shoots
* Bean sprouts
* Beetroot
* Bitter melon
* Bok choy
* Broccoli
* Broccolini
* Brussels sprouts
* Cabbage
* Capsicum
* Carrots
* Cauliflower
* Celeriac
* Celery
* Chard
* Chervil
* Chicory
* Chillies
* Choko
* Choy sum
* Cucumber
* Eggplant
* Endive
* Eschalot
* Fennel
* Garlic
* Ginger
* Gourd
* Green shallots (spring onions)
* Horseradish
* Kale
* Leek
* Lemongrass
* Lettuce
* Mushrooms
* Mushrooms, dried
* Okra
* Onion
* Pak choy
* Pumpkin
* Radish
* Rocket
* Seaweed
* Snow peas
* Snow pea sprouts
* Spinach
* Squash
* String beans
* Sugar snap peas
* Swede
* Tomato
* Tomato passata
* Tomato, semi-dried, not in oil
* Turnip
* Water chestnuts
* Watercress
* Zucchini

WW *meal-prepping* for success

In case this cookbook isn't a big enough clue, at WW we're big fans of this approach to eating – but don't just take our word for it. Here's why planning your meals and then preparing what you can in advance is such a helpful and healthy thing to do – and how to make it work for you.

Feel like you're busy or rushed most of the time? Official statistics show you're in good company. The trouble is that 'busy' is a feeling that can make the hundreds of food decisions we're all expected to make on a daily basis that little bit (or a lot!) more stressful.

It's one of the reasons why research shows that people who plan their meals have healthier diets and weights – it's much easier to eat well when there's a plan in place, especially when life gets hectic because it means 'meals' become one less thing to think about.

And if planning what you're going to eat is the first step towards enjoying healthier meals, prepping ingredients or larger components of those meals, like a bolognese sauce, ahead of time is your insurance policy that you'll actually eat them. Need proof? How about the fact that buying a takeaway at the last minute instead of cooking the food we've stocked our fridges with is one of the main reasons households throw away one out of every five bags of groceries they buy. That's a whole lot of food and money going to waste.

Exactly how you plan and prep your meals will depend on a whole lot of things, including what your lifestyle's like and even how that might change week to week, so don't feel restricted to doing it 'one way'. Still, while there's no one-size-fits all approach, there are some basic strategies to pick and choose from and experiment with so you can make planning and prepping work as well as possible for you.

HOW TO MAKE THE MOST OF MEAL-PLANNING

In its simplest form, meal-planning involves deciding which and how many of your daily meals you want to plan ahead for, and for how many days at a time, before choosing what you're going to cook for each of those meals and making a shopping list (you'll find a template for that on the next page) so you can ensure you have all the ingredients available when you need them.

Tip

Setting aside 10–15 minutes on the same day each week to do this can help turn meal-planning into a regular 'thing'.

There are ways to get even more bang for your meal-planning buck, including this handful of ideas:

* Make the effort to choose recipes and meals that include some of the same ingredients or components, so you can prep and cook once to enjoy several different meals across the week. This could be cooked lentils, roast vegetables or poached chicken breast. You can use the 'ingredient' index at the back of this cookbook to easily find recipes that have foods in common.

* Create a plan that's a little bit flexible. Depending on your preferences (and your personality!), being able to switch and swap a few meals across the week, to cater to what you genuinely feel like eating on any given day rather than being too rigid about what you have to eat, when, can help you stick with the plan.

* Choose recipes that you want and like to eat. Sure, kale, fish and chickpeas are good for you, but if you genuinely don't like the taste of those ingredients, it's best not to choose recipes for your meal plan that rely too heavily on them.

* Incorporate recipes that feature your ZeroPoint foods if you're a WW member. You chose them for a reason – because you like them! So when you do this, you not only tick the box outlined above, you'll be making the most of your PersonalPoints Budget, too.

* Make sure at least one or two (or three!) of the recipes in your meal plan are quick-fire ones so that when your day is busier than expected, you can still create something healthy and delicious, regardless of how much prep you have or haven't been able to do beforehand. Check out the prep and cooking times included on every recipe in this book to guide you.

HOW TO PREP FOR SUCCESS

Once you've planned your meals, the next step is prepping ahead of time to make it as easy as possible to cook those meals. Depending on the ingredients and what suits you best, you can either set aside a specific time to do this prep or simply incorporate it into the cooking process for a particular recipe. Either way, once you start thinking about it, your prepping options are endless, but for some inspiration, you could:

* Chop up ingredients ahead of time. Again, you can either set aside a time to do this or whenever you're preparing meat, plant-based proteins or veggies for one meal, simply chop and divide up more so that you have them ready to go, for another meal. Totally stretched for time? When it comes to vegetables, the frozen variety are great to have on hand. They're nutritious, pre-chopped and you can cook them straight from frozen.

* Cook up double – or triple – batches of those ingredients that the recipes you've chosen have in common. Depending on how many days it'll be until you'll use them again, you can either store them in the fridge or pop them in the freezer (turn over the page for freezing tips). After cooking, 'leftover' ingredients last for two or three days in the fridge.

* Make sure your fridge, freezer and pantry is well organised. The way it's structured only has to make sense to you, but being able to put your hands on the ingredients you need quickly is vital to making the meal-prep and cooking process as easy and enjoyable as possible.

How to get the most out of your freezer

Whether you're storing individual ingredients you've pre-prepped or saving serves of home-cooked meals to eat or repurpose later on, the freezer is your friend. Here's a handful of need-to-know freezing facts.

1 YOUR FREEZER HAS TO BE COLD ENOUGH

The freezing process needs to be fast to minimise the size of the ice crystals that form in food as it's freezing, which is key to maintaining a food's nutrients and texture. To achieve that, set your freezer's temperature at -18°C and avoid overfilling it. Make sure roughly 20 per cent of your freezer's space is always empty, which allows enough cold air to circulate.

2 IF A FOOD'S HOT, YOU'LL NEED TO WAIT A WHILE

It's important not to put piping-hot food straight into the freezer to avoid raising its temperature too much. But don't wait too long – only let food cool until it's just stopped steaming before you freeze it. It's also important to cool cooked ingredients and leftovers as quickly as possible before introducing them to the freezer, which you can do by dividing larger quantities into smaller ones.

3 IT PAYS TO PACK IN PORTIONS

Regardless of whether you're freezing raw or cooked individual ingredients, or fully cooked meals to eat at a later date, always divide food up into serving-sized portions. Why? For food safety reasons you shouldn't refreeze defrosted food (unless it's a raw defrosted food that you've since cooked), so it pays to avoid defrosting more than you need for any one meal. It's also a good idea to label and date food that you put into the freezer, so you know how old it is and can identify it easily.

4 ALWAYS AIM FOR AIRTIGHT

While freezer burn doesn't make a food unsafe to eat, it can affect aspects of a food's quality like its texture. To prevent it occurring on anything you freeze, store the food in an appropriately sized, airtight container and strive to remove as much air as possible from around the food.

5 YOU NEED TO DEFROST FOOD THE RIGHT WAY

When food is frozen quickly the nutrient loss is minimal, but the same can't always be said for what happens during the defrosting process. To minimise the effect, defrost foods that you can't cook from frozen slowly in the fridge. This helps ensure that cells in the food stay intact as any ice crystals thaw, which means less nutrient-rich fluid is lost.

Show some shelf respect

Different foods have different shelf-lives in the freezer:

* Cooked fish: up to 1 month
* Raw oily fish fillets: up to 1 month
* Soups and stews (vegetarian or meat-based): up to 3 months
* Raw lean fish fillets: up to 4 months
* Cooked chicken or meat: up to 6 months
* Roast vegetables: up to 6 months
* Raw chicken pieces: up to 9 months
* Raw meat pieces: up to 12 months
* Raw/blanched vegetables: up to 12 months.

Our smart *swaps*

These simple swaps can give meals a boost of nutrients and flavour without the extra PersonalPoints. Here are some of Rebecca and Wendy's favourite tried-and-tested tips.

* Invest in good-quality **non-stick saucepans and frying pans** so you don't need to add oil when cooking, or use WW oven and pan liners.
* Replace cream and sour cream in both sweet and savoury recipes with **99% fat free plain yoghurt**.
* Use **water or stock** to fry instead of oil (for example, cook off onions and garlic in a tablespoon of water or stock).
* Reduce or replace meat in recipes by swapping some or all of it for diced **non-starchy veggies**, such as carrot, zucchini and mushrooms.
* Always serve main meals with a **side salad or steamed veggies** for extra nutrition and to add a few Points to your daily Budget.
* **You don't need to peel** fruits and vegetables such as potatoes, pumpkin, carrots and apples. Leaving the skin on saves you time and boosts the nutrient content.
* Lower the PersonalPoints of pasta recipes by replacing half the pasta with **spiralised zucchini or pumpkin**; lower it even further by replacing it all.
* Instead of adding cream to soups, **blend them**. This thickens the soup and creates a creamy texture without the extra PersonalPoints.
* Replace butter and oil in cakes and muffins with **99% fat free plain yoghurt.** You can also use **no-added-sugar apple puree** in muffins instead of butter.
* If you're in the mood for an alcoholic beverage, try a **seltzer.** They are very low in PersonalPoints compared to other pre-mixed drinks.
* If you're looking reduce the amount of salt in your diet, try using **herbs and spices** to boost flavour instead.
* Try swapping to **smaller portion sizes**. A good tip is to halve the amount you'd normally want on your plate. Chances are you will realise the portion was enough.
* Don't be put off by the ingredient list – if you don't like or can't eat something, **swap it out.** If you don't like mushrooms, swap them for the same quantity of another non-starchy veggie you do like. If you have an intolerance to something, look up alternatives to use instead.
* Instead of buying fruit-flavoured yoghurt, buy 99% fat-free plain yoghurt and add your own **fresh fruit**.
* Replace butter with **avocado** in your sandwich for a dose of healthy fats.
* Use lettuce leaves instead of **burger buns**.
* Trying swapping out breadcrumbs for flaxseeds if you're **crumbing meat or veggies**. They're a good source of healthy fats and also gluten-free.

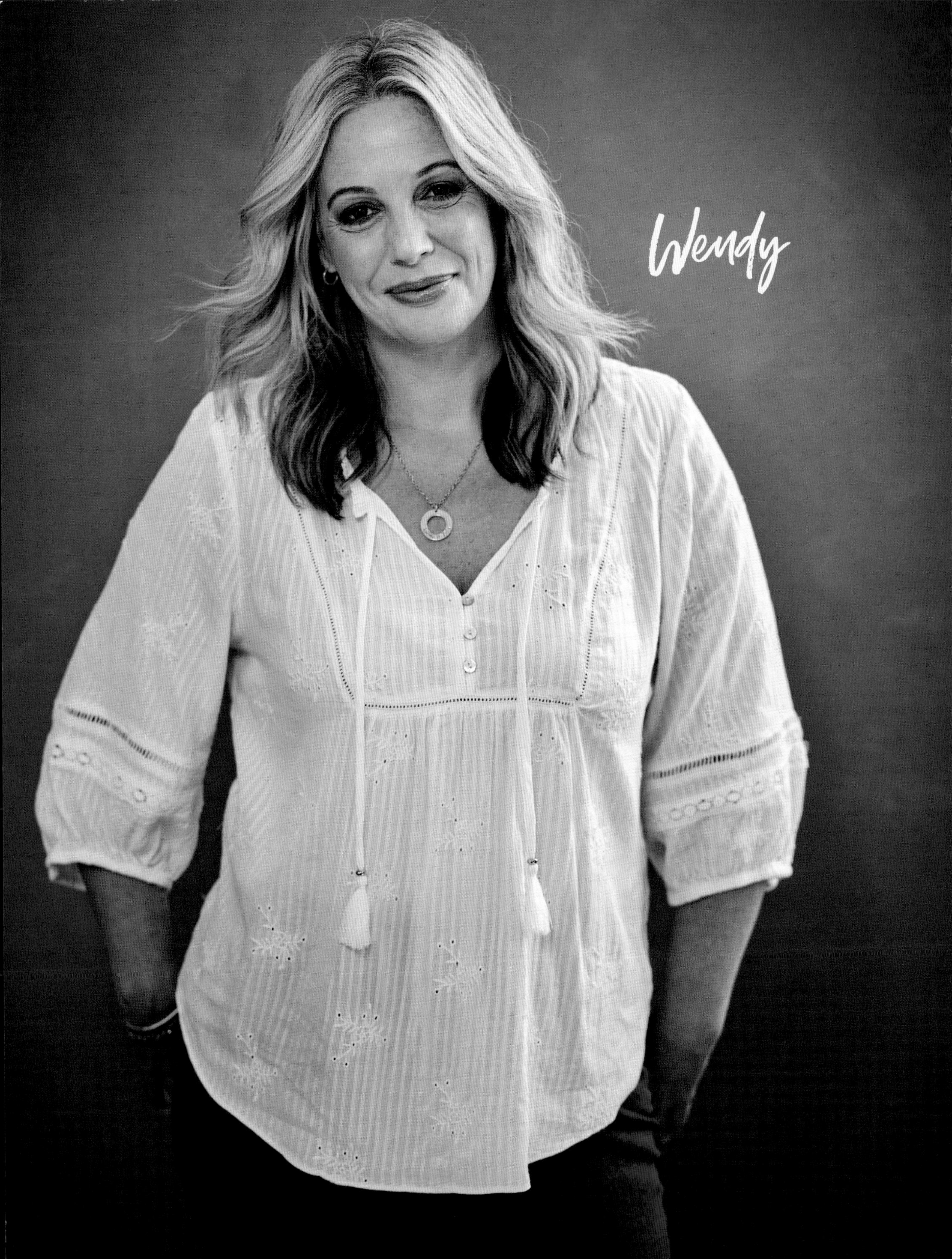

Wendy

Meet your Coaches

Rebecca

Rebecca's *story*

Meet Rebecca from Queensland, aged 44, mum of two and Coach since 2011. Her journey with WW was kickstarted when she saw some candid photos of herself, but a lightbulb realisation a few months later meant losing weight went from being about 'fixing' how she looked for a photo to an investment in her and her family's future. She says it's why she knows that the 28 kg she lost in 18 months is gone for good.

MY LOVE OF COOKING

I grew up in a house that loves food! My mum is a great cook, and I have childhood memories of sitting on the bench while she made delicious-smelling meals, always hoping I was going to be allowed to lick the bowl when chocolate cake was on the menu. She has a talent for whipping up amazing Asian curries and stir-fries, which has strongly influenced my love of 'easy' midweek meals. You know you are never going to walk away from Mum's table feeling hungry! My nana (Mum's mum) was Greek-Australian, so my love of Mediterranean cooking definitely comes from the lamb meatballs that were always cooking away whenever we visited. Then, when I was 10, my granny came out from England to live with us for 12 months. She was an incredible baker, and I fell in love with scones and tea during the many afternoon picnics we had in our garden. My cooking really is an eclectic reflection of all the styles of these strong women in my life.

With this love of cooking came a few extra kilos when I first moved out of home. I love being in the kitchen, pottering around, listening to jazz; however I needed a little help to make my family favourites more waist-friendly. WW gave me this knowledge, and I enjoy tweaking recipes to fit into my PersonalPoints Budget. Now I love that I am able to share my knowledge and passion about eating well with my family, and in my role as a WW Coach I am able to share it with our entire WW community. The ripple effect of my decision to become the healthiest version of myself has been enormous, and I am so honoured to be able to share my story with you.

MY 'WHY'

After the birth of my second child, I'd lost a little bit of weight on my own but while I felt great being able to fit back into my pre-pregnancy clothes, I knew I still wasn't healthy. Plus, I wanted to be an active mum, not a sit-on-the-sidelines mum. I needed to lose weight to be able to keep up with my children.

YOU NAME IT, I'VE TRIED IT

I've tried so many fad diets! From meal replacements and strict calorie-controlled diets to crazy nutrient elimination plans and home-delivered meals, I've done them all. None of them were sustainable, affordable or manageable with a family. WW is completely different because you learn how to cook and eat healthily, how to eat out and how to balance your choices to fit in all the foods you love.

IT WORKS BECAUSE IT'S 'LIFE FRIENDLY'

WW works for me because I can make it fit in with my life. I don't need to eat different meals to my family, I can enjoy eating out or a takeaway meal and I've never felt like I have to give anything up. Plus it's something my whole family can do, which creates a ripple effect of good health for my children.

THE MOMENT I KNEW IT WAS FOREVER

In the past, I'd always had an external reason for wanting to lose weight - a birthday, my wedding, wanting to wear a certain size. But a few months after I joined WW I had a lightbulb moment. I realised that if I made life-long healthier choices, like the ones that WW teaches you, not only would I feel good for those milestone events, I'd feel good all the time. After that, things just clicked. Now, instead of looking at losing weight as being about fitting into a certain size or as a way to 'fix' how I look in photos or at an event, I see this as a life-long commitment to my health and wellbeing - and so I can be present every day for my loved ones. Once I made that mental shift I knew I could be successful long term.

My professional journey

When I reached my goal, I was on maternity leave from my position as a primary school teacher. I knew I didn't want to go back into the classroom with two children under three at home, but I also knew I needed to do something for me, something to get me back into the working world.

Becoming a Coach just made sense. With my education background, and personal experience and achievements with WW, coaching was the right move for me. I wanted to give back to the WW community that had helped support me in such a huge way throughout my journey, so when an opportunity came up to become the Coach for the Workshop I was a member at, I jumped at the chance!

It took me 18 months to lose 28 kg, and I learned so many hints and tips along the way from my fellow members. I love that I am now in a position to share these same hints and tips with members in physical workshops on the Sunshine Coast, and virtual workshops across Australia and New Zealand. The learning journey is continuous, and I also pick up a multitude of ideas from my members, too. Knowledge is power; it is empowering.

I had tried to lose weight on my own previously, but I never seemed to be able to stick with it. I also found that if I just went to WW to weigh in, but not stay for the discussion, I didn't seem to get the same results as when I did stay and learn from my Coach and the other members. The WW community is one of the greatest sources of knowledge and support, and when you can lean on this, you know you are always going to be successful.

A FRIDGE FULL OF FOOD

I love the huge list of go-to ZeroPoint foods on the PersonalPoints program. I know that simply by stocking my fridge with those foods, I'll always have the best choices on hand every day. It's just . . . easy.

My meal-planning is not complicated, and only takes around 20 minutes once a week to write up. For me, breakfast and lunch tend to be similar (such as eggs, overnight oats and salads) so I don't usually formally plan them. I concentrate on dinners as I work a few nights a week, and my kids have quite a few co-curricular commitments. Knowing I can rely on my ZeroPoint foods for a super-fast stir-fry or barbecue means dinner time during the week is never complicated. I love to spend a little more time on my days off creating slightly more elaborate meals, and I use the WW app to create recipes that suit my PersonalPoint Budget by making tweaks and changes to family favourites. I also find that when I meal-plan, we eat a much more interesting and varied diet. I plan at least one vegetarian dinner a week, which not only saves money on meat-based proteins, it adds a couple of extra PersonalPoints to my day!

EXERCISE, BUT NOT AS I KNEW IT

I love being active, but after having my knees and ankle reconstructed five times as a side effect of 15 years of playing competitive netball, I needed to work out how to be active in a way that works for me. WW helped me realise that there are so many ways to exercise that don't require being super fit or that don't put much stress on my joints, things like walking, swimming and yoga. Now, I make an appointment with myself to do something active every day. I put it in my diary and set an alert just like I would for any other appointment. This makes exercise non-negotiable because it just becomes part of my day's to-do list.

3 reasons WW works for Rebecca

1 THE WW APP

The new wellness check-in is fabulous. Having the chance to reflect on the week and nut out what's working well and what I want to change is a wonderful motivator.

2 FAMILY FAVOURITES ARE STILL ON THE MENU

Yep – even pasta and cake! Thanks to WW, I've learned how to recreate some favourite family dishes into healthier versions without sacrificing any of the flavour.

3 THE SUPPORT

I love learning and with WW there's always someone to learn from, whether it's Coaches, members in a workshop or someone on Connect (our members-only digital community) – there's just so much support.

THERE'S SO MUCH TO LOVE ABOUT HOW I FEEL NOW

Losing weight has made a huge difference to my life. I have so much more energy now and I'm no longer in pain with my knee and ankle joints every day. I can walk freely up and down stairs and I can ride a bike and keep up with my kids. I have so much more confidence in myself, too. I'm no longer the person on the sidelines or hiding at the back of a photo. I'm front and centre in my own life and I love it.

Why and how I prep

I started meal-planning after the birth of my first child as a way to save money because we were on a single income. After the birth of my second child, I rejoined WW and put my meal-planning skills to use again, this time incorporating all the tips I picked up in my Workshops.

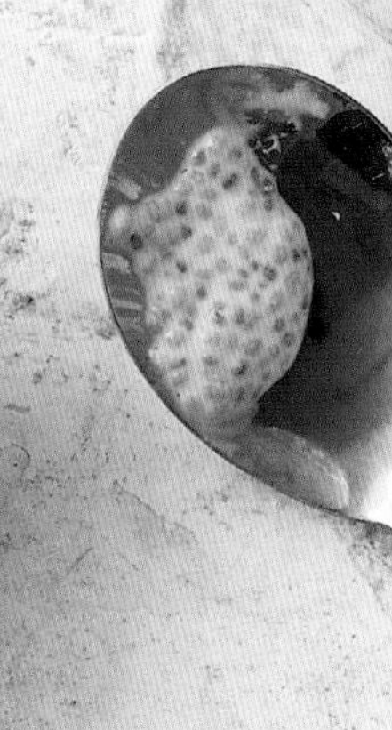

I always meal-plan on Sunday for the coming week. First, I spread out my WW cookbooks on the table; I have the app handy and have the WW meal planner and my shopping list ready to go. I then work out what everyone in my family is doing on each day. All our work/sport/commitments go on the meal planner and I work backwards from that. If we are going to be home late, I plan a slow-cooker meal. If I am not working in the evening, I plan something that takes a little more prep time. My husband loves to barbecue, so if he is home before me, I'll plan a barbecue and salad/veggies meal.

I always get the family involved in the meal choices we put on our plan. Everyone picks one meal they would like to have during the week (that way everyone is happy at least once during the week). I also have the person that picked the meal help with either the meal-prep or, now that my children are older, the cooking of it. This creates a wonderful ripple effect for my children as they are learning lifelong habits about planning, prepping and cooking healthy, nutritious meals.

STEP 1: PLAN

* Gather WW cookbooks, WW app, WW meal planner and a calendar.
* Write all the commitments for the upcoming week on the WW meal planner.
* Everyone chooses one meal to help prep/cook.
* Add meals to WW meal planner, factoring in when everyone is going to be home and time required to prep and cook each meal.

STEP 2: MAKE A LIST

* Write down everything required for all the meals.
* Take the shopping list to the fridge/pantry/ freezer and cross off everything I already have.
* This saves so much money as I'm only buying what we need for the week. It also means I'm sure we have everything I need, so there's no last-minute dashing to the shops (where I always end up buying extra things!) or ordering takeaway meals.

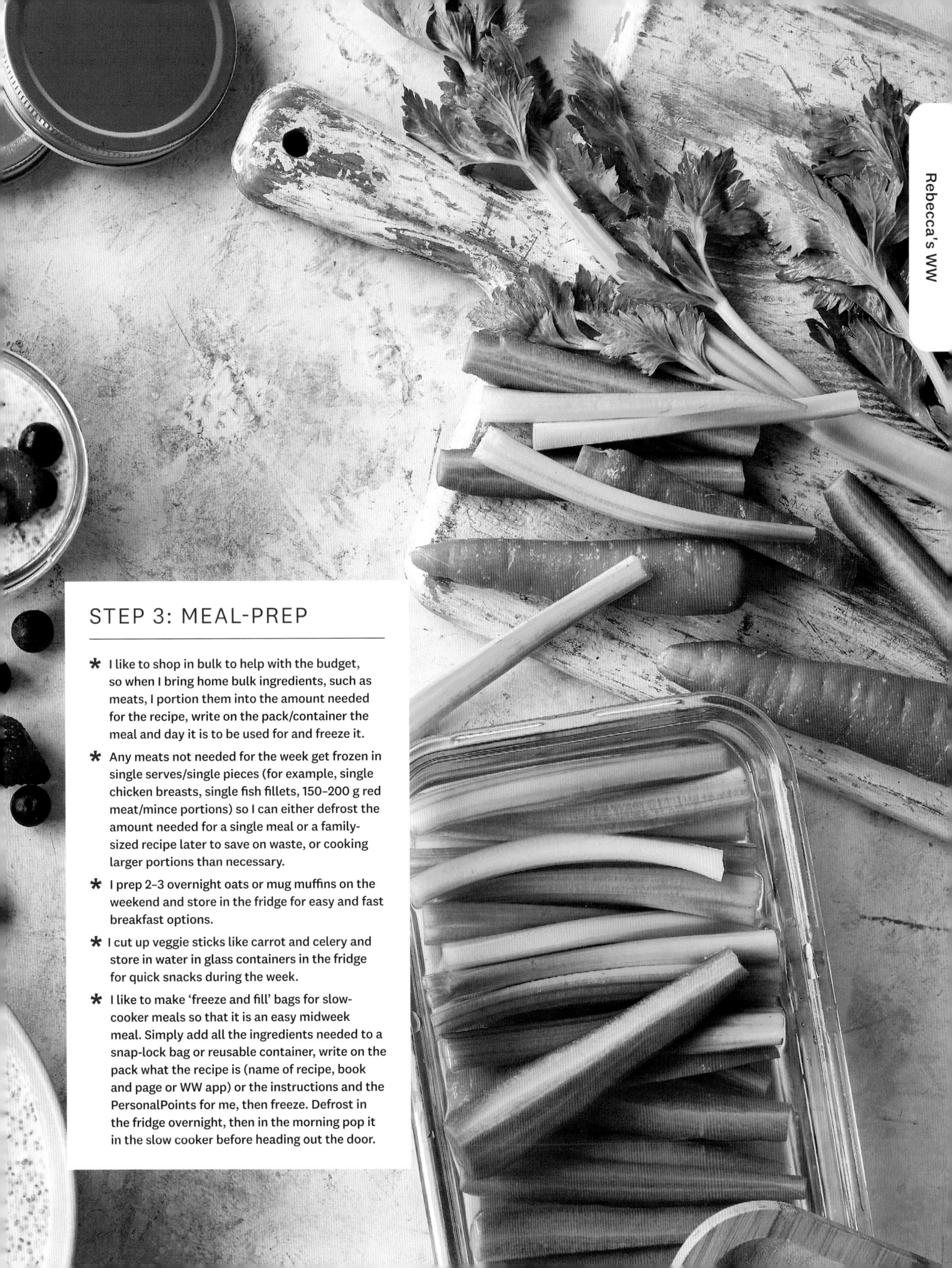

STEP 3: MEAL-PREP

* I like to shop in bulk to help with the budget, so when I bring home bulk ingredients, such as meats, I portion them into the amount needed for the recipe, write on the pack/container the meal and day it is to be used for and freeze it.
* Any meats not needed for the week get frozen in single serves/single pieces (for example, single chicken breasts, single fish fillets, 150–200 g red meat/mince portions) so I can either defrost the amount needed for a single meal or a family-sized recipe later to save on waste, or cooking larger portions than necessary.
* I prep 2–3 overnight oats or mug muffins on the weekend and store in the fridge for easy and fast breakfast options.
* I cut up veggie sticks like carrot and celery and store in water in glass containers in the fridge for quick snacks during the week.
* I like to make 'freeze and fill' bags for slow-cooker meals so that it is an easy midweek meal. Simply add all the ingredients needed to a snap-lock bag or reusable container, write on the pack what the recipe is (name of recipe, book and page or WW app) or the instructions and the PersonalPoints for me, then freeze. Defrost in the fridge overnight, then in the morning pop it in the slow cooker before heading out the door.

Rebecca's *meal-prep* hacks

MY HANDY HINTS

* Poach chicken breasts in the slow cooker to use for sandwiches and salads throughout the week. Do a bulk cook-up, then shred the chicken and freeze it in single portions.

* Cook bulk quantities of plain mince, diced chicken or diced lamb with a base of onion, garlic, salt and pepper, then freeze it in single-serve portions. Defrost when you want it, and flavour with fresh herbs or dried herbs and spices and whatever veggies you have on hand for quick and delicious meals.

* Cook double for lasagne, curry, bolognese and stew recipes and freeze half for another meal.

* My favourite 'cheat's takeaway'? A barbecue chicken from the supermarket teamed with a bagged salad and a mini bake-at-home dinner roll.

* Make 4–5 plain overnight oat jars (just mix the oats and yoghurt/milk together), then flavour with fruit and spices in the morning.

* Batch-cook savoury muffins and mug muffins and freeze in single portions for easy 'grab and go' breakfasts.

* Boil a dozen eggs at the start of the week and store in the fridge.

* Cut veggie sticks (carrot, cucumber, celery) as soon as you get home from shopping and store in water in glass containers in the fridge to keep them crisp all week.

* Have a well-stocked herb and spice cupboard so you can quickly change the flavour of base meals (for example, the base meal is diced chicken, then flavour it with garlic, oregano and basil for Italian; cumin, coriander and paprika for Spanish/Mexican; soy sauce, garlic and ginger for Asian).

* Buy proteins in bulk to save money, then freeze in meal-sized amounts.

MY STORAGE TIPS

* Glass containers keep things cooler so they last longer in the fridge. I store berries in mine, lined with paper towel.

* Freeze in single serves. It makes thawing easier, means you don't have to eat the same thing for days in a row, and saves on waste if it's just one person eating it.

* Label everything clearly: what it is, the date, the PersonalPoints and the recipe book/page it comes from (this ensures the PersonalPoints stay accurate when you change your ZeroPoint food list).

* Label plastic containers with masking tape to avoid damage.

* Fill-and-freeze bags are a huge time-saver and freezer space-saver. Label with the PersonalPoints, cooking instructions, if you need to add any extra ingredients etc, then freeze them flat so they don't take up much room (this also means it is faster to thaw them, too).

* Set up your fridge, pantry and freezer so that the shelf at eye height has all the things you use most often, with the 'treats' on the lower shelves to make them less obvious when you open the door.

* Write the PersonalPoints value of store-bought snacks on the outside of the pack so you can see it clearly when you open the pantry.

The tools I can't live without

* Slow cooker
* Food processor
* Air fryer
* Microplane
* Garlic press
* Mortar and pestle
* Good-quality sharp knives and a knife sharpener
* Good-quality heavy-based non-stick pans
* WW omelette maker and loaf tin.

Rebecca's weekly *meal plan*

	MONDAY	TUESDAY	WEDNESDAY
BREAKFAST	Stove-top baked beans (page 54) 1PP * Prep on weekend	Coconut chia overnight oats (page 50) 11PP * Prep on weekend	Pizza mug muffin (page 196) 4PP * Prep on weekend
LUNCH	Wasabi miso fish bowl (page 90) 7PP	Brown rice tuna sushi rolls (page 100) 4PP	Greek salad jar (page 84) 5PP * Cut extra salad ingredients and store in fridge to serve with tomorrow's lunch
DINNER	Spanish rice (page 158) 12PP	Easy prosciutto-wrapped chicken (page 128) 5PP + side salad	Slow-cooker garlic honey chicken (page 104) 2PP + 1 cup steamed broccoli and cauliflower * Prep in morning
SNACKS	Granny's scones (page 183) 3PP 1 cup baby carrots	Lemon-glazed tea cakes (page 216) 6PP ½ cup cherry tomatoes ½ cup baby cucumbers	Coffee, oat & date loaf (page 213) 4PP 1 cup cherries 2PP
PersonalPoints™ TOTAL	23PP	26PP	17PP
POINTS ADDED FROM NON-STARCHY VEGGIES	4	1	2

THURSDAY	FRIDAY	SATURDAY	SUNDAY
Overnight bircher (page 56) 9PP * Prep on weekend	Quick veggie pan-fry (page 64) + 1 poached egg	Hash brown stack with bacon & eggs (page 70) 6PP	Apple & cinnamon pancakes (page 56) 2PP
Pumpkin & zucchini loaf (page 94) 2PP + salad from yesterday	Chicken sausage rolls (page 78) 3PP * Make on weekend and store in freezer + 1 cup mixed salad leaves	2 x Beef taco cups (page 86) 3PP + 1 cup mixed salad leaves	Chicken & bacon quiche with chickpea crust (page 82) 1PP + side salad
Cauli rice nasi goreng with prawns (page 110) 3PP	Sri Lankan–style salmon curry with turmeric rice (page 110) 8PP Mango & passionfruit mug muffin (page 224) 5PP	Pork fried rice (page 140) 12PP Carrot cake sandwiches with cream cheese icing (page 220) 5PP	Cheat's seafood marinara pizza (page 116) 8PP Raspberry lattice tart (page 218) 6PP
Easy apple & gingerbread cake (page 226) 2PP 125 g raspberries 2PP	Mini cheese & Vegemite scrolls (page 178) 3PP 1 cup celery and capsicum sticks with 1 tablespoon hummus 1PP	Choc-nut energy bliss bites (page 172) 2PP ½ cup button mushrooms and ½ cup cherry tomatoes	Smoked salmon & cream cheese mug muffin (page 197) 2PP 1 cup grapes 4PP
18PP	20PP	28PP	23PP
3	4	3	1

Please note that this is a representation of Rebecca's weekly meal plan, rather than a WW-designed meal plan. PersonalPoints™ values may vary depending on your individualised plan and product brands.

Rebecca's *grocery list*

Here are the foods I keep on hand to make prepping meals easy.

FRESH FRUIT & VEG

- ☐ Apples
- ☐ Fresh berries
- ☐ Medjool dates
- ☐ Red/brown onions
- ☐ Garlic
- ☐ Fresh ginger
- ☐ Baby spinach and rocket mix
- ☐ Baby cos lettuce
- ☐ Broccoli
- ☐ Fresh herbs (flat-leaf parsley, coriander, basil, chives, curry leaves)
- ☐ Carrots
- ☐ Lebanese cucumbers
- ☐ Cherry tomatoes
- ☐ Zucchini
- ☐ Red capsicums
- ☐ Mushrooms
- ☐ Green shallots (spring onions)
- ☐ Butternut pumpkin
- ☐ Cauliflower
- ☐ Potatoes
- ☐ Sweet potato
- ☐ Avocado

MEAT & SEAFOOD

- ☐ Skinless chicken breast fillets
- ☐ Chicken breast mince
- ☐ Turkey breast mince
- ☐ 97% fat-free smoked ham
- ☐ Chorizo sausage
- ☐ Lean short-cut bacon
- ☐ Extra-lean beef mince
- ☐ Lean pork mince
- ☐ Firm white fish fillets
- ☐ Skinless salmon fillets
- ☐ Cooked, peeled prawns
- ☐ Seafood marinara mix

EGGS, DAIRY & ALTERNATIVES

- ☐ Eggs
- ☐ Skim milk
- ☐ Unsweetened cashew milk
- ☐ 99% fat-free plain Greek yoghurt
- ☐ Reduced-fat oil spread
- ☐ Light cream cheese wedges
- ☐ Reduced-fat feta cheese
- ☐ Grated mozzarella cheese
- ☐ Parmesan cheese

FROZEN

- ☐ Peas
- ☐ Reduced-fat puff pastry sheets
- ☐ Wonton wrappers

PANTRY & STAPLES

Seasonings & condiments

- ☐ Dried oregano
- ☐ Mixed dried herbs
- ☐ Onion powder
- ☐ Garlic powder
- ☐ Tuscan seasoning
- ☐ Moroccan seasoning
- ☐ Taco seasoning
- ☐ Smoked paprika
- ☐ Ground turmeric
- ☐ Ground cinnamon
- ☐ Ground cumin
- ☐ Ground coriander
- ☐ Cardamom pods
- ☐ Cinnamon sticks
- ☐ Chinese five spice
- ☐ Dried chilli flakes
- ☐ Mixed spice
- ☐ Black sesame seeds
- ☐ Yellow mustard seeds
- ☐ All-purpose seasoning
- ☐ Saffron
- ☐ Olive oil
- ☐ Garlic-infused olive oil
- ☐ Soy sauce
- ☐ Sesame oil
- ☐ Dijon mustard
- ☐ Miso paste
- ☐ Wasabi paste
- ☐ Fish sauce
- ☐ Chilli paste
- ☐ Oyster sauce
- ☐ Fried shallots
- ☐ Dukkah
- ☐ Nori sheets
- ☐ Sushi seasoning
- ☐ Stock powder
- ☐ Vanilla bean paste
- ☐ Shredded coconut
- ☐ Coconut milk powder
- ☐ Sugar
- ☐ Self-raising flour
- ☐ Cornflour

Canned foods

- ☐ Tuna/salmon/sardines in springwater
- ☐ Tomatoes/tomato paste
- ☐ Black/kalamata olives
- ☐ Asparagus spears
- ☐ Corn

Legumes & grains

- ☐ Chickpeas
- ☐ Cannellini beans
- ☐ Four-bean mix
- ☐ Brown lentils
- ☐ Brown/black rice (including microwave pouches without added oil)
- ☐ Wholemeal pasta
- ☐ Quinoa

Breads & cereals

- ☐ Lebanese bread
- ☐ High-fibre multigrain bread
- ☐ Rolled oats

Snacks

- ☐ Corn thins
- ☐ Hummus

Wendy's *story*

Meet Wendy from Tauranga, New Zealand, aged 45, mum of four awesome kids aged 5, 6, 18 and 22 and WW Coach since 2019. Determined to become a mum who could run around with her young sons rather than watching from the sidelines, Wendy joined WW for them – and herself. What she couldn't see coming was that in the 10 months it took her to lose 25 kg, she would gain enough confidence to take on a new career.

THE REWARDS OF TRANSFORMATION

I know how it feels to want to change your life, but also being scared to. I started my journey as a WW member first and then became a WW Coach. I understand how each member feels the very first time that they walk through those workshop doors. I LOVE watching my members succeed on their WW journey. Watching a person transform mentally and physically is so rewarding. For me, it's a privilege to be trusted to be part of their journey. It's job satisfaction second to none.

MY 'WHY'

I joined WW for myself and for my mental health, but also for my children. I didn't want to miss out on time with my boys, and I didn't want to keep saying no to things because of my weight. I want to be the mum that's on the soccer field, cheering, running and helping. Everything I do, I do for Korban and Luka. Whenever I think about quitting, I remember who's watching. I try and be the best version of myself for my boys.

IT'S A FAMILY AFFAIR

The thing I love about WW is that I don't need to cook several different meals. The same food I want to eat suits the whole family. The best thing is we still eat the same meals we've always enjoyed; they're just healthier versions now. So we'll still have steak and chips with a mushroom sauce, but the steak is grilled instead of fried, the chips are made minus loads of oil and I use yoghurt instead of cream to make the sauce. And because curries have always been a family favourite, now I make a zero PersonalPoints chicken curry (see page 122), which gives me the freedom to enjoy a glass of wine with it too. It's one of the reasons why, in the 10 months it took me to reach my goal weight, I never felt like I was depriving myself of anything.

YOU CAN'T NOT STICK TO THIS

I believe there's not one single thing that's challenging about doing WW. With all the ZeroPoint foods and the simplicity of everything, you can't not stick to it. In the past, I've waged a bit of a war with carbohydrates, treating them as the enemy and believing you couldn't eat them and lose weight at the same time. So I banned them. But because whole grain carbohydrates like pasta and noodles are a ZeroPoint food on my personalised plan, it's given me confidence to eat and enjoy them again – and it's been a real eye opener. I'm eating potatoes and rice and pasta and I've lost weight. That's been such a good learning experience. It may be daunting at first but when you plan your meals and snacks ahead of time, you are less likely to deviate from the plan when hunger strikes. With the introduction of adding PersonalPoints for non-starchy veg on our new

program, I find that I prep loads of veggies now. I have loads of pre-cut (and sometimes even pre-cooked) veg on hand. It is great to have these non-starchy veggies on hand for making quick stir-fries, for making a salad bar station, to fill up my snack box, etc, and add PersonalPoints to my daily Budget too – it's a win-win!

THE WW COMMUNITY IS SOMETHING ELSE

It's amazing. I first joined WW to follow the program online, which suited me because at the time I was quite shy and insecure, and I thought I wanted to do it by myself. But I underestimated how much encouragement I'd need and how much I'd receive from the Connect community. It's simple to access using the WW app and there's always someone on there to motivate and uplift you – they become your WW family.

I'VE GOT A NEW JOB, THANKS TO WW

Given how shy I felt when I first joined WW and that back then the idea of standing up in front of a group of people was incredibly daunting for me, I'm proud to say that I'm now a WW Coach. I run four workshops a week and I have also recently joined the Personal Coaching team. WW Coaching is the best thing I've ever done in my life. I absolutely love it. It isn't just a job to me – it's a true vocation. I have learned so much about myself as a person. From the insecure overweight person I once was to the quiet person I still am today . . . but a person with a voice who no longer allows myself to be walked over. You don't just lose weight at WW: you lose baggage too. You learn new methods and techniques. When I leave the workshop I remove my Coach hat and am a regular member like everyone else and I too have days where I lean on coping techniques that WW has taught me over the years.

I like to remain real on my journey and that is in the public eye and in my workshops too. My WW journey has not been a smooth road, like many members my journey has had many speed bumps, sharp turns, detours and even complete halts: life is not always easy. However, in 2021 I decided to focus on what I can control instead of on what I can't. My co-Coach and dear friend Mandy Gaskell Rowe said to me, 'We might not be able to control what is going on around us, but we can control our WW journey.' That was the switch I so desperately needed. Whenever I feel that I'm falling off the wagon, Mandy's words come to the fore of my mind.

I might not be able to control what's going on around me but I CAN control what I put in my mouth. I CAN track my food diligently. I CAN meal-plan and I CAN continue to reach my weight loss and wellness goals . . . and so can you.

AND I'VE FOUND A 'NEW ME'

I've learned to like myself and I never miss out on pool or beach trips with my children anymore. Thanks to WW, I've got my confidence – and my life – back.

3 reasons Wendy loves WW

1 **THE WAY OF LIFE**
My taste in food has completely changed thanks to WW. Greasy takeaways don't entice me anymore – it's the healthier choices that genuinely appeal to me now.

2 **IT'S FAMILY FRIENDLY**
I don't need to cook several different meals because on WW, the same food I want to eat suits the whole family.

3 **IT WORKS**
For me, there's not one single thing that's been challenging about following the WW program. With all the ZeroPoint foods, and the simplicity of everything, you can't not stick to it.

Why and how I prep

When you've got a plan in place, everything becomes easier on your wellness journey. Meal-prepping has been a big factor in my weight loss. Creating a grocery list to take to the shops not only reduces waste and saves me money, it also keeps me feeling organised and ready for whatever comes my way!

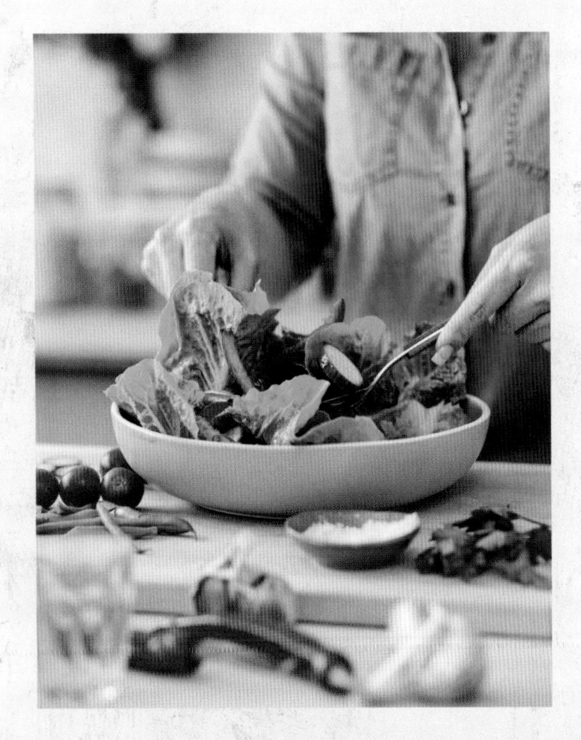

I usually sit down on a Sunday with my meal planner and a few WW cookbooks to decide what will be on the dinner menu for the week ahead. I write down the name of the meal, page number and PersonalPoints. While I'm doing this, I write my grocery list.

I like to cook one meal that the whole family will enjoy at dinner; therefore I always keep their likes and dislikes in mind when deciding on the dinner menu so I don't have to cook separate meals. This has been a huge time-saver that's also helped me on my wellness journey.

I love to cook from scratch and enjoy creating my own recipes. I usually reserve a Friday or Saturday evening to play in the kitchen when my time isn't rushed and there's no meal-prepping involved.

My main tip for meal-planning success is to make a weekly menu and keep notes about how well the menu worked and which dishes were favourites with others in your household, as this will help you with the following weekly menu.

Batch-cooked meals in my freezer (such as my babotie; see page 129) are very handy for dinner, especially on the evenings I have a WW workshop. The last thing I feel like doing is coming home to start cooking from scratch. Having a nutrient-rich, healthy meal on hand discourages me from relying on fast-food.

When I'm creating my meal plan, I usually add the PersonalPoints for breakfast, lunch and dinner, then subtract the total from my daily Budget. I write the remaining PersonalPoints in my snack column: this gives me a lot of freedom as I don't know from day to day what I'm going to feel like. The fact that I'm aware of what I have available in my kitty each and every day is very helpful to me.

The remaining 'snack' PersonalPoints are then used at my leisure on either dessert or a glass or two of wine because, after all, nothing is off limits. This method just works for me!

A meal plan is not set in stone – it's just a guideline to get your work off to a good start. There is nothing wrong with shifting meals around to suit your preferences for that particular day.

TIP 1: PREP BREAKFAST

My mornings are usually very busy with getting two very active young boys ready for school. Make-ahead breakfasts work best for me so that the mornings are more streamlined. I love overnight oats and always have prepared overnight oats in my fridge. I usually make one huge batch that is sufficient to get me through Monday to Friday. What I love about overnight oats is that I can just grab a jar and go. My boys love them too, which really helps on those extra busy mornings as they can each grab a jar and eat their breakfast in the car.

Having a prepared breakfast waiting for me each morning helps me tremendously in reaching my wellness goals for the remainder of the day. It's when breakfast is not prepared that my food choices can really spiral, especially on really busy days. At the weekend, I don't rely on prepared breakfasts. I enjoy spending time in the kitchen on these days as it's less stressful!

TIP 2: CREATE A SALAD BAR

I love Subway sandwiches and have created my own salad-bar station at home. I usually re-fill all the tupperware on a Sunday during my meal-prepping. Each container consists of a delicious filling such as hard-boiled eggs, pre-sliced cheese, tuna mix (see page 97), cucumbers, lettuce, tomatoes, onion, shredded cooked skinless chicken breast, plus my favourite pickles. I use my salad-bar station to fill a low-carb wrap or bread with whatever I fancy, always making sure to include lots of ZeroPoint non-starchy veggies. This is also so handy when I'm making school lunches for the boys, as everything is prepped and ready to go.

TIP 3: FILL SNACK BOXES

I get peckish throughout the day and rely on my snack box to nibble on. I usually allocate myself 3 PersonalPoints. Every day I pack either a 'proper' or 'veg' snack box, as you will see on my meal plan on pages 42–3. Three times a week I will pack a proper snack box, usually if I'm going out for the day and I'm not sure what will be on offer or if there is a school event etc. In this will be two eggs, tuna mix, dates (sometimes filled with something delicious; see page 194 for some of my favourites) and WW chips. I pack a veg snack box on the other days. I fill them with veg so I'm guaranteed to add 2 PersonalPoints to my daily Budget. I use two dividers of the snack box for veg, another for two hard-boiled eggs and another for WW chips.

Wendy's *meal-prep* hacks

MY HANDY HINTS

* Eggs are one of my ZeroPoint foods. I like to boil 6 eggs at a time for the week ahead and keep them refrigerated in an airtight container to use in my snack boxes. I also find it handy to have them already boiled and peeled so that I can slice and add them to my salads or just enjoy them as a quick grab-and-go snack when I'm peckish.

* On the weekend, I prepare breakfast burritos and egg sandwiches to store in the freezer. I also like to freeze cooked fried eggs to use on my breakfast muffins (page 62). I'll leave them to thaw in the fridge overnight, then reheat them gently before serving for an easy breakfast. Not only is it possible to freeze cooked eggs, but I think they actually taste better when reheated than when they're stored in the fridge. While you can freeze cooked eggs for up to a year, I find they taste best within 3–6 months of the freezing date.

MY STORAGE TIPS

* My spices are my must-haves. I store them in glass jars with tight-fitting lids, all in one huge plastic basket in my pantry cupboard. To keep the flavour as long as possible, dried spices and herbs should be kept in a cool, dry place out of direct sunlight – not over the stove as the heat will dull the flavour. With fresh herbs, snip off the base of the stems and remove any discoloured or wilted leaves. Place in a mason jar with an inch of water at the bottom. Seal with the lid and refrigerate. Freezing fresh herbs is also a great time-saver. Rinse, pat them dry and chop as desired. Place in a silicone ice-cube tray and fill with just enough water to cover the herbs before freezing for up to 12 months.

* I like to keep my fridge very organised. My snack boxes and overnight oats are always placed in front so that they're easy to remember to grab each morning. All salads are washed, then chopped or sliced and placed in airtight containers. I also keep sliced and grated cheese to hand as these are my go-to for lunches. I usually check the night before to see what's on the dinner menu and will then thaw my protein overnight and during the day in the fridge. I also keep loads of washed fresh fruit within easy reach – ideal for when boredom strikes and I open the fridge.

* I like to batch-cook oatmeal and pour it into a muffin tin. I then freeze it in the tin, before transferring the portions to a resealable freezer bag. Just heat in the microwave and you're ready to go!

* Freeze ripe bananas before they become mushy. Just chop them up and freeze them in a resealable bag. Use for mug muffins and overnight oats.

* Leftover wine? Freeze it in ice-cube trays. Perfect for cooking!

* I always freeze sliced bread before it goes stale. It's so easy to grab a slice from the freezer and pop it into the toaster on thaw mode.

* Puréed avo freezes really well and can be quickly thawed. It's ideal when making my avo pasta salad (page 80). Just remember to add fresh lemon juice to prevent discolouration.

The tools I can't live without

* **Garlic crusher:** I cook with loads of fresh garlic and always have garlic butter in the fridge. My garlic crusher saves me heaps of time.
* **Kitchen scale and measuring spoons:** I would be totally lost in the kitchen without these. They keep me on track when calculating the PersonalPoints value of foods.
* **Egg timer:** Takes the guesswork out of boiling as my family all enjoy their eggs differently!
* **Mortar and pestle:** Yes, it's heavy, bulky and old-fashioned but I love it. There is nothing more satisfying than making my own spice blends and pastes for my curries. I use mine for chimichurri and flavoured salt too.
* **Microplane:** I love to grate fresh ginger into my curries and lemon zest into my trinchado on page 130 and baked goods.
* **Hamburger freezer set:** I was given this by my dear friend and WW member Danielle. It allows me to make up to 6 burger patties, prep them ahead of time and stack them easily in the fridge or freezer until needed.

Wendy's weekly *meal plan*

	MONDAY	TUESDAY	WEDNESDAY
BREAKFAST	Salted caramel protein overnight oats (page 66) 3PP 2 pieces of fruit	Salted caramel protein overnight oats (page 66) 3PP 2 pieces of fruit	Savoury French toast sandwich (page 68) 5PP 2 pieces of fruit
LUNCH	Deli-style tuna melt (page 97) 5PP 1 cup salad	Low-carb wrap filled with my salad-bar station (page 38) 3PP	Chicken & avo pasta salad (page 80) 4PP
DINNER	Chicken & avo pasta salad (page 80) 4PP	Dad's slow-braised beef (trinchado) (page 130) 5PP 1 glass low-alcohol wine 3PP	Maple-glazed salmon with watermelon & feta salad (page 156) 4PP
SNACKS	Easy oat slice (page 182) 1PP WW soy chips 2PP Instant coffee with skim milk 1PP	No-fuss apple turnover (page 216) 3PP Instant coffee with skim milk 1PP	2 x Chocolate-coated pistachio dates (page 186) 3PP Instant coffee with skim milk 1PP
SNACK BOXES (SEE PAGE 39)	Proper 3PP	Veg 0PP	Veg 0PP
PersonalPoints™ TOTAL	19PP	18PP	17PP
POINTS ADDED FROM NON-STARCHY VEGGIES	1	5	2

THURSDAY	FRIDAY	SATURDAY	SUNDAY
Toast & sugar-free marmalade 4PP 2 pieces of fruit	Salted caramel protein overnight oats (page 66) 3PP 2 pieces of fruit	Freezable egg & bacon muffin (page 62) 8PP 2 pieces of fruit	Strawberry tray bake pancakes (page 72) 4PP 2 pieces of fruit
Freezable egg & bacon muffin (page 62) 8PP 1 cup salad	Low-carb wrap filled with my salad-bar station (page 38) 3PP	Anna's turkey & leek deep dish slice 2PP	Cruskits with hard-boiled eggs 1PP
Anna's slow-cooker Italian steak pizzaiola 5PP	Fakeaway Friday: My go-to chicken curry (page 122) 0PP Spiced rice (page 125) 5PP Garlic naan (page 124) 4PP	Burger made with a store-bought bun & patty & homemade mushroom sauce 7PP Side of steamed veggies	Mince curry & egg pie (babotie) (page 129) 4PP 1 glass low-alcohol wine 3PP
WW protein bar 2PP Instant coffee with skim milk 1PP	Store-bought strawberry cheesecake ice-cream 1PP Instant coffee with skim milk 1PP	Strawberry flummery (page 206) 1PP Instant coffee with skim milk 1PP	60-second lemon mug cake (page 200) 3PP Instant coffee with skim milk 1PP
Proper 3PP	Veg 0PP	Proper 3PP	Veg 0PP
23PP	17PP	22PP	16PP
2	4	3	5

Please note that this is a representation of Rebecca's weekly meal plan, rather than a WW-designed meal plan. PersonalPoints™ values may vary depending on your individualised plan and product brands.

Wendy's *grocery list*

I like to keep all of these foods in my kitchen to make meal-prepping a breeze.

FRESH FRUIT & VEG

- ☐ Bananas
- ☐ Apples
- ☐ Pears
- ☐ PIneapples
- ☐ Oranges
- ☐ Medjool dates
- ☐ Potatoes and sweet potatoes
- ☐ Lettuce
- ☐ Cucumber
- ☐ Tomatoes
- ☐ Avocado
- ☐ Garlic
- ☐ Fresh ginger
- ☐ Fresh herbs (coriander, kaffir lime leaves, flat-leaf parsley, thyme, rosemary)
- ☐ Onions
- ☐ Green shallots (spring onions)
- ☐ Chillies
- ☐ Capsicum
- ☐ Mushrooms
- ☐ Carrots
- ☐ Butternut pumpkin
- ☐ Cabbage

EGGS, DAIRY & ALTERNATIVES

- ☐ Eggs
- ☐ Low-fat or skim milk
- ☐ 99% fat-free yoghurt
- ☐ 97% fat-free cottage cheese
- ☐ Low-fat cheese wedges
- ☐ Low-fat grated cheese
- ☐ Reduced-fat feta
- ☐ Reduced-fat oil spread
- ☐ Light cream cheese
- ☐ Light sour cream

MEAT & SEAFOOD

- ☐ Skinless chicken breast
- ☐ Chicken tenderloin
- ☐ Whole chicken (for roasts!)
- ☐ Mince (lean or extra lean)
- ☐ Venison
- ☐ Beef rump steak
- ☐ Luncheon meat
- ☐ Bacon
- ☐ Salmon
- ☐ Prawns
- ☐ Mussels
- ☐ Seafood marinara mix

PANTRY & STAPLES

Seasonings & condiments

- ☐ Ground turmeric
- ☐ Cumin seeds
- ☐ Garam masala
- ☐ Kashmiri masala
- ☐ Curry powder
- ☐ Dried chilli flakes
- ☐ Cinnamon sticks
- ☐ Mustard powder
- ☐ Paprika
- ☐ Cardamom pods
- ☐ Chinese five spice
- ☐ All spice
- ☐ Ground nutmeg
- ☐ Ground coriander
- ☐ Ground cinnamon
- ☐ Mustard seeds
- ☐ Ground ginger
- ☐ Onion powder
- ☐ Garlic powder
- ☐ Dried rosemary
- ☐ Dried thyme
- ☐ Dried mixed herbs
- ☐ Dried bay leaves
- ☐ Dried basil
- ☐ Reduced-sugar tomato sauce
- ☐ Whole grain mustard
- ☐ English mustard
- ☐ Dijon mustard
- ☐ Red wine vinegar
- ☐ Balsamic vinegar
- ☐ Soy sauce
- ☐ Fish sauce
- ☐ Sesame oil
- ☐ Chilli oil
- ☐ Cooking spray
- ☐ Tabasco sauce
- ☐ Low-fat mayo
- ☐ Sugar-free maple syrup
- ☐ Marmite
- ☐ Olives
- ☐ Gherkins
- ☐ Pickled onions
- ☐ Anchovies

Canned foods

- ☐ Diced and whole peeled tomatoes
- ☐ Tuna in springwater
- ☐ Kidney beans
- ☐ Butter beans
- ☐ Low-sodium stock
- ☐ Fruit in juice

Legumes & grains

- ☐ Basmati/jasmine rice
- ☐ Brown rice
- ☐ Wholemeal pasta

Breads & cereals

- ☐ Wholemeal bread
- ☐ Low-carb wraps
- ☐ Weet-Bix
- ☐ Bran cereal (high fibre)
- ☐ Rolled oats

Snacks

- ☐ Whole grain rice crackers
- ☐ Crispbreads
- ☐ Popcorn
- ☐ Dried apricots and figs
- ☐ Sunflower seeds
- ☐ Natural peanut butter
- ☐ Low-sugar jelly

FROZEN

- ☐ Veg, including spinach, cauliflower, carrots and peas
- ☐ Prawns
- ☐ Lean beef burger patties
- ☐ Bread
- ☐ Strawberries
- ☐ Ice cream
- ☐ WW frozen meals

Recipes

Breakfast

Coconut chia *overnight* oats

3-11 **PersonalPoints range per serve** 

Five minutes of prep in the evening and your future self will thank you in the morning! I usually have two or three jars ready to go in the fridge for a super-speedy breakfast before racing off out the door, or as a filling and delicious dessert at the end of the day.

REBECCA

Serves *1* / ***Prep*** *5 minutes + chilling*

⅓ cup (30 g) rolled oats
1 tablespoon (15 g) chia seeds
70 g 99% fat-free plain Greek yoghurt
½ cup (125 ml) unsweetened cashew milk
½ teaspoon vanilla bean paste
2 medjool dates, pitted and finely chopped
½ teaspoon shredded coconut, plus ½ teaspoon extra to serve
60 g fresh berries, to serve

1 Mix oats, chia seeds, yoghurt, milk, vanilla, dates and coconut in a glass jar (or WW reusable storage cup) until well combined. Seal with lid and refrigerate overnight.

2 Top with berries and extra coconut to serve.

- TO REFRIGERATE: Store for up to 3 days. Top with berries and extra coconut just before serving.

Rebecca's tip

If you can't find unsweetened cashew milk, replace with unsweetened coconut, soy or almond milk.

See page 9 for details

Strawberry cereal breakfast muffins

2-5 **PersonalPoints range per muffin** 

These wholesome muffins with crisp, golden tops are as pretty as they are delicious. Perfect for breakfast or a tea-time snack.

WENDY

Makes 6 / *Prep* 10 minutes / *Cook* 20 minutes

- **1½ cups (70 g) mixed grain cereal flakes (see tip)**
- **½ cup (45 g) rolled oats**
- **¼ teaspoon bicarbonate of soda**
- **½ teaspoon baking powder**
- **2 large bananas, mashed**
- **2 eggs, lightly beaten**
- **1 teaspoon vanilla essence**
- **⅓ cup (85 g) reduced-sugar strawberry jam**
- **2 fresh strawberries, sliced**

1 Preheat oven to 180°C.

2 Use your hands to coarsely crush cereal in a large bowl. Stir in oats, bicarbonate of soda and baking powder. Make a well in the centre, then add banana, eggs and vanilla. Stir to combine. Gently stir through jam to create a swirl in the mixture.

3 Line a 6-hole ⅓ cup (80 ml) capacity muffin tray with paper cases. Divide the mixture evenly among paper cases. Top with strawberry slices. Bake for 20 minutes or until just firm in the centre when lightly touched with fingertips. Stand muffins in tray for 5 minutes, then transfer to a wire rack to cool.

- TO STORE: Keep muffins at room temperate in a reusable container lined with a paper towel for up to 4 days.
- TO FREEZE: Store muffins in a reusable container for up to 3 months. Thaw at room temperature or microwave individual frozen muffins until warm.

Wendy's tip

I used Special K for these muffins, but you can use any flaked breakfast cereal.

See page 9 for details

Stove-top baked *beans*

0-3 **PersonalPoints range per serve** 

Homemade baked beans are a billion times tastier than their commercially made counterparts. I love serving mine over toasted multigrain bread or with a soft poached egg for a quick breakfast, lunch or dinner.

REBECCA

Serves 4 / *Prep* 10 minutes / *Cook* 15 minutes

- 1 small brown onion, finely chopped
- 2 button mushrooms, finely chopped
- 2 x 400 g cans butter beans, drained and rinsed
- 2 tablespoons (45 g) tomato paste
- 1 teaspoon smoked paprika
- 2 teaspoons ground turmeric
- 1 tablespoon (20 ml) soy sauce or tamari
- 2 teaspoons Dijon mustard

1 Heat a non-stick saucepan over medium heat. Cook onion, stirring, for 2–3 minutes, until softened.

2 Stir in remaining ingredients. Season with salt and pepper. Bring to the boil, then reduce heat and simmer for about 10 minutes, stirring occasionally, until mushrooms are tender. Serve.

- **TO REFRIGERATE:** Store cooked beans in a reusable container for up to 3 days. Reheat in a saucepan, adding a splash of water and stirring occasionally until thoroughly heated through, or reheat individual portions in the microwave.
- **TO FREEZE:** Store as above for up to 2 months. Thaw overnight in the fridge. Reheat as above.

Rebecca's tip

Add a little water in step 2 as the liquid absorbs, to prevent mixture catching on the base of pan.

See page 9 for details

Berry flake breakfast bars

Waking up to a breakfast ready to go is the best way to start the day. You can take these bars straight from the freezer and microwave them to heat up. I also like to add a drizzle of sugar-free maple syrup if I'm feeling extra sweet.

WENDY

Makes 6 / *Prep* 10 minutes / *Cook* 30 minutes

1 cup (85 g) WW berry flakes cereal
30 g self-raising flour
1 teaspoon baking powder
4 medjool dates, pitted and finely chopped
200 g mashed banana (see tip)
1 egg, lightly beaten
50 ml skim milk

1 Preheat oven to 180°C. Lightly spray a 6-hole ¾ cup (180 ml) capacity non-stick mini loaf mould tray with oil.

2 Combine cereal flakes, flour, baking powder and dates in a large bowl. Add banana, egg and milk. Stir until combined.

3 Spoon mixture evenly into prepared moulds. Bake for 25–30 minutes or until a skewer inserted into the centre of bars comes out clean. Stand bars in tray for 5 minutes, then transfer to a wire rack to cool.

- **TO REFRIGERATE:** Store bars in a reusable container for up to 1 week.
- **TO FREEZE:** Store bars as above for up to 3 months. Thaw at room temperature or microwave individual frozen bars until warm.

Wendy's tip

You'll need about 2 medium bananas to get 200 g mashed banana.

See page 9 for details

Apple & cinnamon *pancakes*

2 **PersonalPoints per pancake** 

Apple and cinnamon are a match made in heaven, so my apple and cinnamon pancakes just make sense! I usually make a double batch and store half in the freezer for a delicious addition to lunch boxes during the week.

REBECCA

Makes *12* / ***Prep*** *10 minutes* / ***Cook*** *15 minutes*

1 large red or green apple, unpeeled, finely grated
1 teaspoon ground cinnamon
1 cup (150 g) self-raising flour
1 cup (250 ml) skim milk
1 egg

1. Whisk all ingredients in a bowl until smooth.
2. Lightly spray a large non-stick frying pan with oil and heat over medium heat.
3. Pour 4 x ¼ cupfuls of the batter into hot pan to make 4 pancakes. Cook for 2–3 minutes, until bubbles appear on the surface. Turn pancakes and cook the other sides for 1–2 minutes, until golden. Transfer pancakes to a plate and cover to keep warm. Repeat with remaining batter to make 12 pancakes in total. Serve warm.

- **TO REFRIGERATE:** Store pancakes in a reusable container for up to 3 days. To serve, reheat in microwave, air fryer or sandwich press, or enjoy cold.
- **TO FREEZE:** Store in a reusable container, with a piece of baking paper between each pancake, for up to 3 months. Thaw at room temperature and reheat as above.

Rebecca's tip

You could also cook all 12 pancakes at once on a barbecue hot plate.

See page 9 for details

Avo pancakes

3-4 PersonalPoints range per pancake

These slightly savoury pancakes are as delicious as they are healthy. The avo adds a subtle green hue and delivers an extra hit of healthy fat for your day. Serve with poached eggs or crispy bacon for a luxury café-style treat.

WENDY

Makes 8 / *Prep* 15 minutes / *Cook* 35 minutes

- 1 medium avocado, chopped
- 1⅓ cups (200 g) plain flour
- 2 teaspoons baking powder
- 2 eggs
- ½ cup (125 ml) unsweetened almond milk
- ½ cup fresh basil leaves
- 1 tablespoon lemon juice

1 Blend all ingredients in a blender until smooth and well combined.

2 Lightly spray a non-stick frying pan with oil (or use the WW non-stick pan liner) and heat over medium–low heat. Pour ¼ cup of the batter into hot pan. Cook for about 3 minutes or until browned underneath. Turn and cook until other side is browned and pancake is cooked through. Transfer to a plate and cover to keep warm. Repeat with remaining batter to make 8 pancakes in total. Serve warm.

- **TO REFRIGERATE:** Store pancakes in a reusable container for up to 3 days. To serve, reheat in microwave, air fryer or sandwich press, or enjoy cold.
- **TO FREEZE:** Store in a reusable container, with a piece of baking paper between each pancake, for up to 1 month. Thaw at room temperature and reheat as above.

Wendy's tip

If you find the pancake batter is too thick, try adding a little more milk to loosen.

See page 9 for details

Cheese & bacon *breakfast* muffins

3-4 PersonalPoints range per muffin

These little beauties are a quick and tasty way to start your day. Make them fresh or whip up a batch and store them in the fridge or freezer for an easy grab-and-go brekky on your way out the door.

REBECCA

Makes 6 / *Prep* 15 minutes / *Cook* 25 minutes

- ⅔ cup (105 g) wholemeal self-raising flour
- 1 teaspoon baking powder
- 2 eggs, lightly beaten
- ¼ cup (60 ml) skim milk
- 100 g short-cut bacon, fat trimmed, finely chopped
- 3 green shallots (spring onions), thinly sliced
- 1 zucchini, grated
- 6 cherry tomatoes, chopped
- 10 g grated parmesan cheese

1. Preheat oven to 180°C. Lightly spray a 6-hole ¾ cup (180 ml) capacity non-stick Texas or Jumbo muffin tray with oil. Wipe out excess oil with paper towel.

2. Combine flour and baking powder in a bowl. Stir in eggs and milk. Season with salt and pepper, then fold through bacon and vegetables. Spoon batter evenly into prepared muffin tray and sprinkle with parmesan.

3. Bake for 20–25 minutes or until muffins are golden and just firm in the centre. Stand muffins in tray for 5 minutes, then remove and serve warm.

- **TO REFRIGERATE:** Store muffins in a reusable container for up to 5 days. Warm in microwave to serve.
- **TO FREEZE:** Store muffins as above for up to 3 months. Warm frozen muffins in microwave to serve.

See page 9 for details

Overnight *bircher*

2-9 PersonalPoints range per serve 

No-cook breakfasts are my saviour on busy mornings – even better is one you have already prepped! Dating back to the early 1900s, bircher muesli is the original overnight oats. Mine is a nod to the traditional recipe, and a fantastically easy way to start your day.

REBECCA

Serves *2* / ***Prep*** *5 minutes + chilling*

- ⅔ cup (60 g) rolled oats
- 150 g 99% fat-free plain Greek yoghurt
- ⅔ cup (160 ml) skim milk
- 2 medjool dates, pitted and finely chopped
- 1 red or green apple, unpeeled, grated
- 1 teaspoon ground cinnamon
- 2 teaspoons shredded coconut
- 1 cup (160 g) fresh berries

1. Mix all ingredients, except berries, in a bowl until well combined. Divide mixture evenly between 2 glass jars or reusable containers. Seal with lids and refrigerate overnight.
2. Top with berries to serve.

- **TO REFRIGERATE:** Store bircher for up to 4 days. Top with berries just before serving.

Rebecca's tip

Fresh berries can be replaced with thawed frozen berries or any other fruit of your choice.

See page 9 for details

Freezable egg & bacon muffins

These hearty egg and bacon muffins are a deliciously easy grab'n'go breakfast. You can prep and freeze them whole in advance to have mornings sorted for busy days ahead. Double or triple the recipe to keep the entire family fed.

WENDY

Makes *6* / ***Prep*** *15 minutes* / ***Cook*** *10 minutes*

6 eggs
6 x 25 g slices short-cut bacon, fat trimmed
6 x 21 g slices light cheddar cheese
6 x 65 g wholemeal English muffins, split in half

1 Preheat oven to 200°C. Lightly spray a shallow-sided non-stick baking tray with oil (or line it with a WW oven liner). Heat prepared tray in the preheated oven for 15 minutes.

2 Remove tray from oven. Crack eggs, one at a time, onto the hot tray. Season with salt and pepper. Bake for about 6 minutes or until eggs are cooked to your liking. Remove from oven. Cool eggs on tray.

3 Meanwhile, lightly spray a large non-stick frying pan with oil and heat over medium-high heat. Cook bacon for about 1 minute on each side or until crisp and light golden. Drain on a paper towel-lined plate and cool.

4 To assemble, sandwich cheese slices, bacon and eggs between muffin halves to make 6 muffins in total. Serve straight away or wrap each filled muffin individually and follow freezing instructions below.

- TO FREEZE: Store wrapped muffins in a reusable freezer bag or container for up to 3 months. Thaw overnight in the fridge. To serve, reheat individual muffins in microwave on High (100%) for 1 minute or until hot.

See page 9 for details

Quick *veggie* pan-fry

0 PersonalPoints per serve

Eating enough veg each day can be a challenge, but packing them in at brekky is one easy way to get ahead. Enter my veggie-packed pan-fry! I love serving this with soft poached eggs, dark rye toast and avocado for a more filling meal.

REBECCA

***Serves** 4 / **Prep** 10 minutes / **Cook** 10 minutes*

- **1 garlic clove, crushed**
- **1 brown onion, finely chopped**
- **2 zucchini, chopped**
- **3 tomatoes, chopped**
- **1 teaspoon dukkah**
- **1 teaspoon dried chilli flakes**
- **2 tablespoons (40 ml) soy sauce or tamari**
- **Fresh coriander sprigs, to serve (optional)**

1. Heat a large non-stick frying pan over medium heat. Cook garlic and onion with a splash of water, stirring, for 3–4 minutes, until softened

2. Stir in zucchini, tomatoes, dukkah, chilli and soy sauce. Season with salt and pepper. Reduce heat, cover and cook for 3–4 minutes, until vegetables are tender. Scatter over coriander sprigs (if using), to serve.

- TO REFRIGERATE: Store in a reusable container in the fridge for up to 2 days. Reheat in microwave or in a saucepan over medium heat until hot.

- TO FREEZE: Store single servings in reusable containers for up to 6 months. Thaw in fridge overnight and reheat as above, adding a little water if needed.

Rebecca's tip

Keep a batch of this in the freezer to use as a quick vegetarian pasta sauce.

See page 9 for details

Salted caramel protein *overnight oats*

3-9 **PersonalPoints range per serve** 

Starting out with a satisfying breakfast means I'm much more likely to make better choices for the rest of the day. Prepping overnight oats in advance is something I make a point of doing each week, as it helps to keep me on track. As well as being rich in protein and fibre, these oats are deliciously sweet and salty.

WENDY

Serves 1 / Prep 10 minutes + chilling

- 1 small banana, mashed
- 130 g 99% fat-free plain yoghurt
- 20 g rolled oats
- 1 teaspoon vanilla essence
- ⅓ cup (80 ml) no-added-sugar salted caramel topping
- 1 WW caramel protein bar

1. Combine banana, yoghurt, oats, vanilla and 2 tablespoons caramel topping in a small bowl.
2. Finely grate three-quarters of the protein bar and stir through oat mixture. Spoon half the mixture into a 1 cup (250 ml) capacity glass jar or serving glass. Drizzle over half the caramel topping, then spoon in remaining oat mixture. Drizzle over remaining caramel topping. Roughly chop remaining protein bar and scatter on top of oats. Cover and refrigerate for about 3 hours, until chilled, or overnight.

- **TO REFRIGERATE:** Store oats for up to 5 days. Top with chopped protein bar just before serving. The longer the oats sit in the fridge, the softer they will become.

Wendy's tip

Increase the recipe to make as many servings as you want for the week ahead.

See page 9 for details

Savoury French toast sandwich

5-8 **PersonalPoints range per sandwich** 

Bread dipped in egg and fried is always a winner. This is a great breakfast to have in the freezer for those days when you don't have much time – just pop it in the toaster to reheat and off you go.

WENDY

Makes 1 / *Prep* 5 minutes / *Cook* 15 minutes

2 eggs
½ teaspoon dried mixed herbs
2 x 38 g slices low-carb whole grain bread

1 Place eggs and herbs in a bowl. Season with salt and pepper and whisk well.

2 Lightly spray a non-stick frying pan with oil and heat over medium heat. Dip 1 bread slice in egg mixture, then transfer to hot pan. Cook for about 3 minutes on each side until golden brown. Transfer to a plate. Lightly spray pan again with oil and repeat step with the other slice of bread, reserving any leftover egg mixture.

3 Leave the second bread slice in pan and top with the first cooked bread slice. Pour over any leftover egg mixture and cook for a further 1–2 minutes, until egg is set. Use an egg slide or spatula to lightly press slices together. Serve.

- TO FREEZE: Skip step 3 and finish recipe at end of step 2. Place a sheet of baking paper between each slice, then wrap sandwich in foil and place in a reusable snap-lock bag for up to 1 month. To reheat, remove frozen sandwich from foil and separate slices. Place in toaster or sandwich press until warmed through and crisp. Sandwich back together to eat, or enjoy as toast.

Wendy's tips

- To get ahead on prep, whisk the eggs the night before, then cover and refrigerate.
- For sweet French toast, add 1 teaspoon sugar to the egg mixture instead of salt and pepper.

See page 9 for details

Hash brown stacks with bacon & eggs

5-8 **PersonalPoints range per serve** 

Golden, veggie-packed hash browns, served with crispy bacon and runny eggs . . . Does it get any better? This recipe makes an impressive breakfast for a lazy weekend morning. The hash browns can be made ahead of time and warmed through before serving.

REBECCA

Serves *4* / ***Prep*** *25 minutes* / ***Cook*** *25 minutes*

- 200 g potato, peeled
- 200 g orange sweet potato (kumara), peeled, grated
- 400 g pumpkin, peeled, grated
- 1 large zucchini, grated, excess liquid squeezed out
- 1 small red onion, finely chopped
- ¼ cup chopped fresh flat-leaf parsley
- ½ cup (40 g) grated parmesan cheese
- 1 tablespoon all-purpose seasoning
- 5 eggs
- 4 x 25 g slices short-cut bacon, fat trimmed

1. Steam the whole potato for 6 minutes. Set aside until cool enough to handle, then grate and transfer to a large bowl. Add sweet potato, pumpkin, zucchini, onion, parsley, parmesan, seasoning and 1 egg. Season with salt and pepper and mix well. Shape mixture into 8 even-sized rounds, about 8–10 cm in diameter.

2. Lightly spray a large non-stick frying pan or barbecue plate with oil and heat over medium–high heat. Cook hash browns in two batches for about 5–6 minutes on each side, until golden brown and cooked through. Transfer to a large non-stick tray and keep warm in a 160°C oven.

3. Add bacon to the same frying pan or barbecue plate over medium–high heat. Cook for 1–2 minutes on each side, until crisp and golden. Transfer to tray with hash browns. Crack the remaining eggs into pan or onto barbecue plate. Cook for about 3 minutes or until cooked to your liking.

4. To create the stack, place 1 hash brown on a plate, top with 1 slice of bacon, another hash brown, then an egg. Repeat to make 4 stacks in total.

- **TO REFRIGERATE:** Store hash browns in a reusable container, with baking paper between layers, for up to 4 days. Cook bacon and eggs just before serving.
- **TO FREEZE:** Store hash browns as above for up to 3 months. Reheat from frozen in microwave or on a baking tray in a 180°C oven.

See page 9 for details

Strawberry *tray bake* pancakes

This is the most fuss-free way to enjoy pancakes any day of the week – you simply whip up the batter and pop it in the oven. My recipe is inspired by Yussy, who has a lovely food Instagram account.

WENDY

Serves 12 / *Prep* 10 minutes / *Cook* 15 minutes

1¾ cups (265 g) plain flour
1½ tablespoons monk fruit sweetener
1 teaspoon baking powder
½ teaspoon bicarbonate of soda
1 cup (250 ml) buttermilk
1 egg, lightly beaten
¼ cup (60 ml) sugar-free maple syrup
2 tablespoons (40 g) reduced-fat oil spread, melted
200 g fresh strawberries, sliced
1 teaspoon icing sugar

1. Preheat oven to 200°C. Lightly spray a 20 cm x 30 cm shallow ovenproof dish with oil.

2. Place flour, sweetener, baking powder and bicarbonate of soda in a large bowl and make a well in the centre. Add buttermilk, egg, syrup and oil spread. Whisk until well combined. Pour batter into prepared dish and top with strawberries.

3. Bake for 15 minutes or until set in the centre and lightly golden. Dust with icing sugar. Cut into 12 pieces to serve.

- TO REFRIGERATE: Store baked pancakes, covered, in dish, for up to 3 days. Microwave individual pancakes until warm to serve.
- TO FREEZE: Store baked pancakes in a single layer in a reusable container for up to 1 month. To serve, microwave individual frozen pancakes until warm.

Wendy's tip

If you can't find buttermilk, substitute with 1 cup (250 ml) skim milk mixed with 3 teaspoons lemon juice or white vinegar. Allow the mixture to rest for 5 minutes, or until the milk has slightly thickened.

See page 9 for details

Lunch

Bang bang chicken salad

4–8 PersonalPoints range per serve 

I really can't stress how much I love Sichuan cuisine and bang bang chicken salad is one of my personal favourites. This recipe is my low-PersonalPoints version, with the secret being my homemade Sichuan sauce!

Serves 4 / *Prep* 15 minutes

- 600 g shredded cooked skinless chicken breast
- 400 g packet fresh coleslaw (no dressing)
- 150 ml Sichuan sauce (see opposite)
- 125 g cherry tomatoes, halved
- 1 green shallot (spring onion), thinly sliced
- Fresh coriander sprigs, to serve

1. Place chicken and coleslaw in a large bowl. Season with salt and toss well. Cover and refrigerate until ready to serve.

2. To serve, pour Sichuan sauce over chicken and coleslaw mixture and toss to lightly coat. Transfer to a serving plate. Scatter over tomatoes, shallot and coriander sprigs.

- TO REFRIGERATE: Store combined chicken and coleslaw, without sauce, covered for up to 6 hours. Toss with sauce and transfer to serving plate with tomatoes, shallot and coriander just before serving.

See page 9 for details

Sichuan sauce

4 PersonalPoints per serve 

I'm a huge fan of Sichuan sauce but the store-bought versions tend to contain a lot of added sugars, so I prefer to make my own. This recipe is so fast and full of punchy flavour. It has a multitude of uses, but my favourite is as a salad dressing or marinade.

Serves 10 (about 40 ml per serve) / *Prep* 10 minutes

- ⅓ cup (80 ml) soy sauce or tamari
- ¼ cup (60 ml) sesame oil
- ¼ cup (60 ml) chilli oil
- ⅓ cup (80 ml) rice wine vinegar
- 4 garlic cloves, crushed
- 2 tablespoons lime juice
- 1½ tablespoons ground ginger
- 3 teaspoons ground black peppercorns
- 3 teaspoons ground coriander

1. Mix all ingredients in a jug until well combined. Pour mixture into a clean glass jar, seal with lid and refrigerate. Give the jar a good shake before serving.

- TO REFRIGERATE: Store sauce in a sealed jar for up to 2 weeks.
- TO FREEZE: Pour into a silicone ice-cube tray, cover and store for up to 4 months. Thaw individual portions at room temperature.

Wendy's tip

I use Asian-style chilli oil, available from supermarkets and Asian grocery stores.

See page 9 for details

Chicken sausage rolls

3-4 **PersonalPoints range per sausage roll** 

My chicken sausage rolls are a healthier version of everyone's favourite snack, thanks to the lean chicken breast mince and loads of veggies. From prep to table in under an hour, these little morsels are perfect for a tasty midweek dinner or popping into lunch boxes. My kids also love them cold, straight from the fridge, for an easy snack after school.

REBECCA

Makes 24 / *Prep* 20 minutes / *Cook* 30 minutes

- 500 g chicken breast mince
- 2 large carrots, grated
- 2 large zucchini, grated
- 1 brown onion, grated
- 2 garlic cloves, crushed
- 2 teaspoons dried mixed herbs
- 1 tablespoon (20 ml) barbecue sauce
- 4 x 170 g sheets frozen reduced-fat puff pastry
- 2 teaspoons black sesame seeds

1 Preheat oven to 200°C. Line 2 baking trays with baking paper.

2 Place mince, vegetables, garlic, herbs and barbecue sauce in a large bowl. Season with salt and pepper and mix until well combined.

3 Cut each pastry sheet in half to give 8 rectangular strips in total. Place one-eighth of the chicken mixture along the long edge of 1 pastry strip. Roll up from filled edge to enclose filling. Place seam-side down and cut evenly into 3 pieces. Continue with remaining pastry and chicken mixture to make 24 sausage rolls in total.

4 Arrange rolls, seam-side down, on prepared trays. Sprinkle with sesame seeds. Bake for 25–30 minutes, or until crisp and golden.

- TO REFRIGERATE: Store sausage rolls in a large reusable container, with baking paper between each layer, for up to 3 days. Reheat on baking trays in a 180°C oven until filling is hot in the centre.
- TO FREEZE: Store as above for up to 2 months. Reheat from frozen, as above.

See page 9 for details

Chicken & avo pasta salad

3-5 **PersonalPoints range per serve** 

This flavourful pasta salad using my own healthy creamy avo sauce is just perfect for a quick lunch or light dinner, especially on a hot day.

Serves *4* / ***Prep*** *10 minutes*

2 cups (310 g) cooked farfalle pasta
250 g shredded cooked skinless chicken breast (see tip)
1 green capsicum, finely chopped
½ red onion, finely chopped
1 large Lebanese cucumber, chopped
1 serve (70 g) Creamy avo sauce (see opposite)
1 teaspoon finely shredded lemon zest
Fresh basil leaves, to serve

1 Place pasta, chicken, capsicum, onion and cucumber in a large bowl. Add Creamy avo sauce and stir to combine.

2 Divide among 4 reusable containers or jars. Sprinkle with lemon zest and basil leaves. Serve straight away or drizzle a layer of lemon or lime juice over the surface, cover with plastic wrap, then lid and refrigerate. Drain off the juice before serving.

- TO REFRIGERATE: Store following instructions in step 2 for up to 1 day.

See page 9 for details

Creamy avo sauce

0-2 **PersonalPoints range per serve**  

This sauce is a great healthy alternative to a cream-based pasta sauce or shop-bought salad dressing. A good source of healthy fats and whipped up in just 5 minutes, it's sure to become a staple in your kitchen. To prevent it turning brown in the fridge, be sure to follow the instructions.

Serves *4* / ***Prep*** *5 minutes*

1 large avocado, chopped
⅓ cup (80 g) 99% fat-free plain yoghurt
2 garlic cloves
½ cup fresh basil leaves
1 teaspoon finely grated lemon zest

1 Process all ingredients in a food processor or blender until smooth and well combined. Season with salt and pepper.

- TO REFRIGERATE: Transfer sauce to a reusable container. Drizzle a layer of lemon or lime juice over the surface, cover with plastic wrap, then lid and store for up to 5 days. Drain off the juice before serving. If sauce has thickened, stir through a little warm water until it reaches desired consistency.

Wendy's tip

To cook my chicken, I season a skinless chicken breast with coarsely ground salt and pepper, then microwave it on High (100%) for 8 minutes. Cool it slightly before shredding, chopping or slicing.

See page 9 for details

Chicken & bacon quiches with chickpea crust

1-6 **PersonalPoints range per quiche** 

I LOVE quiche. What I don't love is the high PersonalPoints value of traditional pastry bases with rich, creamy fillings, and filo pastry bases just don't cut it for me. Made from chickpeas, my quiche base is a tasty, fibre-filled, low-PersonalPoints delight. Give it a try!

REBECCA

Makes 6 / *Prep* 25 minutes / *Cook* 40 minutes

2 x 400 g cans chickpeas, drained and rinsed
1 teaspoon onion powder
1 teaspoon garlic powder
1 teaspoon stock powder
1 teaspoon dried mixed herbs
1 extra-large egg

FILLING
1 zucchini, grated
1 carrot, grated
1 green shallot (spring onion), thinly sliced
2 x 25 g slices short-cut bacon, fat trimmed, chopped
150 g shredded cooked skinless chicken breast
6 extra-large eggs

1. Preheat oven to 170°C. Lightly spray 6 x 11 cm round, loose-base non-stick flan tins with oil and place on a baking tray.

2. Process chickpeas, onion powder, garlic powder, stock powder, mixed herbs and egg in a food processor until smooth. Divide mixture evenly between the prepared flan tins. Using damp fingers, press the mixture evenly over the base and side of the tins. Bake for 15 minutes until lightly browned and set. Remove from oven.

3. For the filling, divide zucchini, carrot, shallot, bacon and chicken evenly among the chickpea crusts. Place eggs in a bowl, season with salt and pepper and whisk well. Pour evenly over filling in each flan tin. Return to oven and bake for 25 minutes or until filling is set and light golden.

- TO REFRIGERATE: Store cooked quiches in a container for up to 2 days. Serve cold or reheat in the oven or microwave until hot.
- TO FREEZE: Leave cooked crusts in tins and store in a large reusable container, with baking paper between each crust, for up to 2 months. When ready to cook quiches, transfer flan tins to baking trays, add filling to frozen crusts and bake as directed in step 3.

Rebecca's tip

If preferred, use a large 24 cm flan tin instead of the 6 small flan tins, increasing cooking times for crust to 20–25 minutes and filling to 30 minutes.

See page 9 for details

Avocado boat *prawn cocktails*

1-3 PersonalPoints range per boat 

Juicy prawns in creamy seafood cocktail sauce and served in a ripe avocado is an elegant appetiser to serve to guests. Or enjoy it as a light lunch option that you can whip up in just 10 minutes.

WENDY

Makes 4 / *Prep* 10 minutes

- ¼ cup (60 g) 99% fat-free plain yoghurt
- 1 tablespoon (20 ml) reduced-sugar tomato sauce
- 1 tablespoon (25 g) low-fat mayonnaise
- 3 teaspoons Worcestershire sauce
- 200 g cooked king prawns, peeled, deveined
- 2 small avocados, halved
- 1 pinch paprika
- 2 teaspoons fresh dill sprigs
- 1 lime, cut into wedges

1 Mix yoghurt, tomato sauce, mayonnaise and Worcestershire sauce in a bowl until well combined. Add prawns and season with salt and pepper. Mix to coat prawns in dressing.

2 Fill avocado halves with prawn mixture. Sprinkle with paprika and garnish with dill. Serve with lime wedges.

- TO REFRIGERATE: Complete step 1 up to 6 hours ahead and store, covered. Halve avocados and add prawn filling just before serving.

Wendy's tips

- To ensure the avocado halves sit flat on plates for serving, cut a thin slice off the base.
- Be sure to check the Worcestershire sauce label if you follow a gluten-free diet, as some contain gluten.

See page 9 for details

Greek salad jar

5-6 **PersonalPoints range per jar** 

Salad jars are the ultimate prep-ahead meals. You can get a few days of lunches prepped and in the fridge in just 15 minutes. Layering your jar so all the wet ingredients are at the bottom and the salad leaves are at the top means your salad will stay nice and crisp.

REBECCA

Makes 4 / Prep 15 minutes

400 g can chickpeas, drained and rinsed
250 g cherry tomatoes, quartered
1 large Lebanese cucumber, chopped
50 g pitted kalamata olives, chopped
½ red onion, thinly sliced
100 g reduced-fat feta cheese, crumbled
8 baby cos lettuce leaves, chopped

DRESSING
⅓ cup (80 ml) freshly squeezed lemon juice
1 tablespoon (20 ml) olive oil
1 garlic clove, crushed
1 teaspoon dried oregano

1 To make dressing, place lemon juice, olive oil, garlic and oregano in a small jar. Season with salt and pepper, seal with lid and shake well. Divide dressing evenly between 4 x 2 cup (500 ml) capacity glass jars or reusable containers.

2 Layer chickpeas, tomatoes, cucumber, olives, onion, feta and lettuce evenly in jars. Place lids on jars and store in the fridge for up to 3 days.

- TO REFRIGERATE: Store sealed salad jars as above.

Rebecca's tip

For extra protein, add 400 g lean cooked lamb leg steaks, cut into thin strips and layer on top of chickpeas.

See page 9 for details

Beef *taco* cups

2 PersonalPoints per cup 

This recipe was inspired by my son's request to take tacos to his end-of-season football party a few years ago. Made using wonton wrappers, these cups are everything you love about tacos, served in an easy-to-go package. Enjoy!

REBECCA

***Makes** 24 / **Prep** 30 minutes / **Cook** 40 minutes*

- 1 brown onion, finely chopped
- 500 g extra-lean beef mince
- 400 g can four-bean mix, drained and rinsed
- 2 carrots, grated
- 2 zucchini, grated
- 400 g can diced tomatoes
- 35 g packet taco seasoning
- 24 x 10 g wonton wrappers
- ½ medium avocado, chopped
- 1 tablespoon thinly sliced fresh chives

1. To make filling, heat a large non-stick frying pan over medium heat. Cook onion, stirring, for about 5 minutes or until softened. Add mince and cook, stirring to break up lumps, until browned. Stir in beans, carrot, zucchini, tomatoes and seasoning. Bring to the boil, then reduce heat and simmer for 30 minutes, stirring occasionally.

2. Meanwhile, preheat oven to 180°C. Lightly spray 2 x 12-hole ½ cup (125 ml) capacity muffin trays with oil. Press a wonton wrapper into each prepared hole. Bake for 6–7 minutes, until crisp and golden.

3. Fill each wonton cup with hot filling. Top with avocado and chives to serve.

- TO REFRIGERATE: Store cooked, unfilled wonton cases in a reusable container for up to 3 days. Store cooked filling in a separate container for up to 2 days. Reheat filling in a non-stick frying pan over medium heat, adding a splash of water and stirring occasionally until thoroughly heated through. Fill and top wonton cases just before serving.

- TO FREEZE: Store filling as above for up to 1 month. Thaw overnight in the fridge. Reheat as above.

Rebecca's tip

This recipe can also be made in a pie maker. Cook the wrappers for 2 minutes, then add filling and cook for a further 5 minutes. Top with avocado and chives to serve.

See page 9 for details

Mum's *curried* pasta salad

8–9 **PersonalPoints range per serve** 

A recipe very close to my heart, this is my mum's curried pasta salad. It was always offered at every barbecue when I was growing up. It's perfect to prep ahead as the flavours develop while it rests in the fridge.

WENDY

Serves 4 / *Prep* 15 minutes / *Cook* 10 minutes

200 g penne pasta
185 g can tuna in springwater, drained, flaked
410 g can peaches in natural juice, drained and chopped
1 red capsicum, finely chopped
1 red onion, finely chopped
2 teaspoons ground turmeric
1 tablespoon curry powder
1 teaspoon caster sugar
2 tablespoons (50 g) low-fat mayonnaise
⅓ cup (80 g) 99% fat-free plain yoghurt
2 tablespoons chopped fresh flat-leaf parsley

1. Cook pasta in a large saucepan of boiling salted water, following packet instructions, or until al dente. Drain. Refresh under cold running water and drain well.

2. Mix cooked pasta, tuna, peaches, capsicum, onion, spices, sugar, mayonnaise and yoghurt in a large bowl until well combined. Season with salt and pepper. Serve sprinkled with parsley.

- TO REFRIGERATE: Store salad in a reusable container for up to 2 days.

See page 9 for details

Wasabi miso *fish bowl*

1-11 PersonalPoints range per serve 

If your family likes sushi, this deconstructed version in a bowl will save you the rolling time! Try it as a really quick and easy veggie-packed lunch-box option or a no-fuss midweek dinner.

REBECCA

***Serves** 4 / **Prep** 20 minutes + marinating / **Cook** 6 minutes*

- 4 x 150 g firm skinless white fish fillets, cut into 5 cm pieces
- 2 cups (340 g) cooked black rice
- 1 medium avocado, sliced
- 4 cups (80 g) baby spinach and rocket mix
- ½ red onion, thinly sliced
- 2 carrots, grated
- 1 Lebanese cucumber, thinly sliced
- 100 g cherry tomatoes, quartered

WASABI MISO MARINADE

- 2 tablespoons (50 g) white miso paste
- 2 teaspoons wasabi
- 2 tablespoons (40 ml) soy sauce or tamari
- 1 garlic clove, crushed
- 1 teaspoon finely grated fresh ginger

1. To make marinade, mix miso, wasabi, soy sauce, garlic and ginger with ¼ cup (60 ml) water in a bowl. Add fish and turn to coat in marinade. Cover and refrigerate for 30 minutes.

2. Heat a non-stick frying pan or barbecue hot plate over medium-high heat. Cook fish, for about 2-3 minutes on each side or until cooked through.

3. Divide rice, avocado, spinach and rocket, onion, carrot, cucumber and tomatoes evenly among 4 shallow serving bowls. Top with fish and serve.

- TO REFRIGERATE: Cook fish 1 day ahead, cover and refrigerate. Prepare salad ingredients up to 6 hours ahead and arrange with fish in reusable containers or bento boxes. For lunch on the move, transport with an ice pack to keep fresh.

Rebecca's tips

- You can swap fish for chicken or tofu.
- To save time, use microwaveable black rice, but be sure to check the PersonalPoints in the WW app.

See page 9 for details

Deconstructed burger bowl

10-13 **PersonalPoints range per serve** 

My grain-free burger bowl is a healthy way to enjoy all the flavours of a burger and chips, without the bun. You can easily increase the quantities if you're catering for the whole family.

WENDY

Serves 1 / *Prep* 10 minutes / *Cook* 20 minutes

- 100 g frozen crinkle-cut chips
- 2 lettuce leaves, shredded
- 1 tomato, sliced
- ¼ red onion, thinly sliced
- 2 slices (80 g) fresh pineapple, halved
- 2 portobello mushrooms, sliced
- 21 g slice light cheddar cheese, cut into quarters
- 1 teaspoon balsamic glaze
- 1 x cooked Curried chicken patty (page 145), cut into quarters

1 Cook frozen chips following packet instructions.

2 Meanwhile, arrange lettuce, tomato, onion, pineapple, mushrooms and cheese in a large shallow bowl and drizzle with balsamic glaze. Add chips and patty to bowl to serve.

- TO REFRIGERATE: Store salad ingredients in bowl or a reusable container, covered, for up 4 hours ahead. Drizzle salad with balsamic glaze and add cooked chips and patty just before serving.

Wendy's tip

You can use any type of burger patty in this recipe. For more ideas, turn to page 142.

See page 9 for details

Pumpkin & zucchini loaf

1-2 **PersonalPoints range per serve**

Is it just me, or does everyone always end up with leftover veggies after a roast?! A great way to use them up is to make my super-easy veggie loaf. Perfect for a light meal or lunch box filler and equally delicious served warm or cold.

REBECCA

Serves 8 / *Prep* 15 minutes / *Cook* 55 minutes

150 g cooked butternut pumpkin, cut into 2 cm pieces
1 zucchini, grated
½ red onion, chopped
1 tablespoon chopped fresh flat-leaf parsley
1 tablespoon chopped fresh basil
8 eggs
¼ cup (20 g) grated parmesan cheese

1 Preheat oven to 170°C.

2 Mix pumpkin, zucchini, onion and herbs in a large bowl.

3 Whisk eggs and parmesan in a bowl. Season with salt and pepper. Add to pumpkin mixture and stir to combine. Pour mixture into a lightly oiled and baking paper-lined 12 cm x 22 cm loaf tin (or a WW silicone loaf tin).

4 Bake for 40-45 minutes, until set and golden. Stand in the tin for 10 minutes before turning out. Cut into 8 slices to serve.

- TO REFRIGERATE: Store sliced loaf in a reusable container for up to 4 days. Serve cold or reheat in microwave.
- TO FREEZE: Store sliced loaf as above, with baking paper between slices, for up to 3 months. Thaw slices on a paper towel-lined plate, covered, in the fridge or reheat in microwave.

Rebecca's tip

If you don't have cooked pumpkin, boil, steam or microwave raw pumpkin until just tender, then drain and mix with veggies in step 2.

See page 9 for details

Roasted  & rice pie

6-9 **PersonalPoints range per serve**

This veggie rice pie is one of my favourite easy meal-prep recipes. Similar to my 'Bottom of the fridge' pasta bake on page 112, it's a great way to use up all the veggies you have left over at the end of the week. And it tastes amazing! Freeze single serves for a fast lunch option.

REBECCA

Serves 4 / *Prep* 20 minutes / *Cook* 1 hour

- 3 cups (450 g) chopped fresh vegetables (see tip)
- 300 g butternut pumpkin, peeled, cut into 1 cm thick slices
- 2 teaspoons garlic-infused extra-virgin olive oil
- 1 tablespoon dried Italian herbs
- 1 cup (170 g) cooked brown rice
- 50 g semi-dried tomatoes (not in oil), drained, chopped
- 10 pitted kalamata olives, chopped
- 3 eggs, lightly beaten
- 1 cup (120 g) grated mozzarella cheese

1. Preheat oven to 180°C. Line 2 baking trays with baking paper.

2. Spread chopped vegetables over 1 prepared tray and arrange the pumpkin slices in a single layer over the other prepared tray. Drizzle 1 teaspoon oil over vegetables on each tray, then sprinkle evenly with dried herbs and season with salt and pepper. Bake for 30 minutes or until vegetables are tender.

3. Lightly spray a 20 cm round springform tin with oil and line base and side with baking paper. Place on a baking tray. Arrange pumpkin slices in a layer over the base of prepared tin.

4. Transfer roasted chopped vegetables to a large bowl. Add rice, semi-dried tomatoes, olives and eggs and stir to combine. Spoon mixture over pumpkin in tin. Smooth the top and sprinkle with mozzarella. Bake for 20–30 minutes or until golden and set in centre. Serve cut into wedges.

- TO REFRIGERATE: Store pie, covered in tin, for up to 4 days. Uncover and serve cold or reheat in a 150°C oven for 25–30 minutes, until hot in centre, or reheat individual servings in microwave.
- TO FREEZE: Cut pie into single serves and freeze in reusable containers for up to 3 months. Thaw in fridge overnight, then reheat in microwave or serve cold.

Rebecca's tips

- Use a combination of whatever vegetables you have in your fridge.
- If you don't have garlic-infused oil, use plain olive oil and add 1 crushed garlic clove over the vegetables in step 2.

See page 9 for details

Deli-style tuna melts

4–5 **PersonalPoints range per serve** 

Tuna lovers! Meet my ultimate melt. This tuna mix is a staple in my fridge – I use it for sandwiches, toasties and salads. For something a little bit different, turn to page 188 for my Tuna melt bites.

WENDY

Serves *4* / ***Prep*** *15 minutes* / ***Cook*** *3 minutes*

4 x 35 g slices whole grain bread
½ cup (60 g) grated mozzarella cheese

TUNA MIX
185 g can tuna in springwater, drained and flaked
1 small red onion, finely chopped
1 tablespoon chopped fresh flat-leaf parsley
1 garlic clove, crushed
1 teaspoon whole grain mustard
50 g 99% fat-free plain yoghurt

1 For the tuna mix, combine all ingredients in a small bowl. Season with salt and pepper and mix well.

2 Spread tuna mixture evenly over bread slices and top with mozzarella. Cook under a preheated grill or in an air fryer until cheese is melted. Season to taste with extra pepper to serve.

- TO REFRIGERATE: Store tuna mixture in a reusable container for up to 2 days.

Wendy's tip

If you like spice like me, try topping with a dash of Tabasco sauce.

See page 9 for details

Bacon & veggie slice

This is a really nutrient-packed and tasty recipe, which can be varied to suit your taste buds. When I'm short for time I use my food processor instead of grating the veggies. Perfect to team with a side salad for an easy lunch or dinner, or cut into bite-sized pieces to go into your snack box.

REBECCA

Serves 6 / *Prep* 20 minutes / *Cook* 40 minutes

- 2 brown onions, finely chopped
- 4 carrots, grated
- 3 zucchini, grated
- 150 g whole cup mushrooms, sliced
- 2 garlic cloves, crushed
- 2 tablespoons chopped fresh flat-leaf parsley
- 125 g short-cut bacon rashers, fat trimmed, chopped
- ¼ cup (20 g) grated parmesan cheese
- 8 large eggs, lightly beaten
- 1 teaspoon smoked paprika

1. Preheat oven to 180°C. Lightly spray a 23 cm x 35 cm x 3 cm deep baking tin with oil. Line base and sides with baking paper.

2. Place all ingredients in a large bowl, season with salt and pepper and mix well. Pour mixture into prepared tin and smooth the top.

3. Bake for 30–40 minutes, until golden brown and set. Cut into 6 pieces. Serve warm or cold.

- TO REFRIGERATE: Store slice in a reusable container for up to 4 days. Enjoy cold or reheat individual servings in microwave.

- TO FREEZE: Store individual slices in reusable containers or snap-lock bags for up to 3 months. Thaw on a paper towel–lined plate, covered, in fridge overnight. Reheat in microwave or serve cold.

Rebecca's tip

Serve with baby rocket leaves on the side to add more PersonalPoints to your Budget.

See page 9 for details

Brown rice tuna *sushi rolls*

1-4 PersonalPoints range per roll 

Using brown rice over white rice in these sushi rolls not only increases the fibre content, but also adds a slightly nutty flavour that I really love. To make the prep easier, I cook the rice the night before and store it in the fridge so it is ready to go in the morning, then I get my kids involved in assembling and rolling the sushi.

REBECCA

***Makes** 8 / **Prep** 1 hour / **Cook** 5 minutes*

- 3 cups (510 g) cooked brown rice, chilled
- ⅓ cup (80 ml) sushi seasoning
- 8 nori sheets
- 185 g can tuna in springwater, drained, flaked
- 2 carrots, grated
- 8 cooked asparagus spears (fresh or canned)
- 1 Lebanese cucumber, cut into 8 batons

1. Place rice in a large bowl. Sprinkle over the sushi seasoning and mix well to coat rice evenly.
2. Place a nori sheet, shiny-side down, on a bamboo sushi mat or large sheet of baking paper. Using wet fingers, spread one-eighth of the rice over the nori sheet, leaving a 2 cm border across the top.
3. Spread one-eighth of the tuna across the edge closest to you, then top with one-eighth of the carrot, 1 asparagus spear and 1 cucumber baton.
4. Using the mat or baking paper as a guide, roll up nori firmly from the edge closest to you to enclose the filling. Moisten the border of the nori sheet with water to seal the roll. Repeat with remaining ingredients to make 8 rolls in total.
5. Use a serrated knife to cut rolls in half or cut into 2 cm thick slices, if preferred. Serve.

- TO REFRIGERATE: Wrap whole sushi rolls individually in foil and store in a reusable container for up to 2 days. Cut in half or into slices to serve.

Rebecca's tip

Serve with soy sauce for dipping, with pickled ginger and wasabi on the side.

See page 9 for details

S&B
WASABI
PREPARED WASABI IN TUBE
KEEP REFRIGERATED AFTER OPENING.
WASABI

Dinner

Slow-cooker garlic honey chicken

2-4 **PersonalPoints range per serve** 

Coming home at the end of the day to a delicious bowl of comfort food is my idea of heaven. I usually make a double batch of this recipe so I can freeze the leftovers in single portions for quick meals during busy times.

REBECCA

Serves 4 / *Prep* 15 minutes / *Cook* 2 hours 45 minutes – 5 hours 15 minutes

- ⅓ cup (80 ml) soy sauce or tamari
- 2 tablespoons (45 g) tomato paste
- 1 tablespoon (20 g) honey
- ½ teaspoon Chinese five spice
- 4 garlic cloves, crushed
- 1 tablespoon grated fresh ginger
- ¼ teaspoon dried chilli flakes
- 500 g skinless chicken breast, cut into 3 cm pieces
- 250 g broccoli, chopped
- 125 g mushrooms, sliced
- 1 large carrot, sliced
- 1 zucchini, sliced
- 1 tablespoon (10 g) cornflour
- ½ cup fresh coriander sprigs

1 Whisk soy sauce, tomato paste, honey, spice, garlic, ginger and chilli in a small bowl.

2 Place chicken and vegetables in a 5.5 litre (22 cup) capacity slow cooker. Pour over the sauce mixture and stir to combine. Season with salt and pepper. Cook on low for 4–5 hours (or high for 2.5–3 hours), until chicken is cooked through.

3 Mix cornflour with 1 tablespoon water in a small bowl until smooth, then stir through chicken and vegetables in slow cooker. Cook on high for a further 15 minutes or until sauce has thickened.

4 Scatter over coriander sprigs to serve.

- **TO REFRIGERATE:** Transfer garlic honey chicken to a large reusable container or divide individual portions into separate reusable containers. Store for up to 2 days. To reheat, simmer gently in a saucepan or microwave single servings until hot, stirring in a little water if sauce is too thick.
- **TO FREEZE:** Store garlic honey chicken as above for up to 3 months. Thaw overnight in the fridge. Reheat as above.

See page 9 for details

Lemon & thyme pork *schnitzels*

3 PersonalPoints per serve

My dar's (grandfather's) family originated in Germany. Before joining the Australian army and serving in Papua New Guinea, Dar was a baker in a small Queensland country town, creating beautiful loaves of bread. So these lemon and thyme pork schnitzels are a nod to both Dar's heritage and his profession.

REBECCA

Serves 6 / *Prep* 20 minutes / *Cook* 25 minutes

- 6 x 140 g lean pork leg steaks, fat trimmed
- 1 cup (60 g) panko breadcrumbs
- 1 teaspoon finely grated lemon zest
- 1 tablespoon chopped fresh thyme leaves
- ⅓ cup (80 g) 99% fat-free plain natural yoghurt

1 Preheat oven to 180°C. Line a large baking tray with baking paper.

2 Pound steaks between two sheets of baking paper with the flat side of a meat mallet or a rolling pin until about 5 mm thick. Season with salt and pepper.

3 Combine panko, lemon zest and thyme on a large plate or in a large shallow dish. Season with salt and pepper. Place yoghurt in a separate large shallow dish.

4 Working with 1 steak at a time, dip steaks in yoghurt to lightly coat both sides, then coat evenly in panko mixture, pressing on lightly with fingertips.

5 Transfer schnitzel to prepared tray in a single layer and lightly spray with oil. Bake for 20–25 minutes, until golden and cooked through. Serve.

- **TO REFRIGERATE:** Store uncooked, crumbed schnitzel, covered, on prepared tray for up to 1 day. Uncover and bake as required. Store cooked schnitzel in a reusable container for up to 3 days.
- **TO FREEZE:** Store uncooked, crumbed schnitzel or cooked schnitzel in a large reusable container with baking paper between each schnitzel for up to 2 months. Thaw frozen uncooked schnitzel in fridge overnight, then cook as instructed in step 5. To reheat cooked schnitzel, place on a tray in a 180°C oven until hot.

Rebecca's tips

- Serve with a side of steamed green veggies and lemon wedges.
- If using a thick yoghurt, thin to the consistency of pouring cream with a little water.

See page 9 for details

Chicken & mushroom *filo pie*

2-5 **PersonalPoints range per serve** 

This is true comfort food. A classic creamy chicken and mushroom pie, turned just that little bit healthier by switching to light and crispy filo pastry and replacing cream with yoghurt. Enjoy!

WENDY

Serves 4 / *Prep* 15 minutes / *Cook* 50 minutes

2 teaspoons beef stock powder
1 teaspoon onion powder
150 g 99% fat-free plain yoghurt
1 red onion, finely chopped
500 g button mushrooms, sliced
600 g skinless chicken breasts, cut into 2 cm pieces
3 garlic cloves, crushed
2 teaspoons finely chopped fresh thyme
4 fresh filo pastry sheets

1 Preheat oven to 180°C.

2 Mix stock powder, onion powder and yoghurt in a small bowl until combined. Set aside.

3 Lightly spray a large non-stick frying pan with oil and heat over medium heat. Cook onion and mushrooms, stirring occasionally, for 8–10 minutes, until softened. Add chicken, garlic and thyme. Cook, stirring occasionally, for a further 10 minutes or until the chicken is just cooked through. Remove from heat, stir in yoghurt mixture and season with salt and pepper.

4 Lightly spray a 1 litre (4 cup) capacity, 22 cm round ovenproof dish with oil and line with 3 sheets of filo. Fold any overhanging filo into the dish. Fill the dish with chicken mixture. Tear the remaining filo sheet into large pieces, gently scrunch and place on top to completely cover filling. Lightly spray the top with oil. Bake for 30 minutes or until pastry is golden.

- **TO REFRIGERATE:** Store prepared pie, covered in dish, for up to 2 days. Uncover and bake as required, adding an extra 5 minutes cooking time.

See page 9 for details

Sri Lankan-style salmon curry with turmeric rice

1-18 **PersonalPoints range per serve** 

Growing up, whenever my mum hosted a dinner party she would spend hours in the kitchen making a beautiful Sri Lankan seafood curry. It was her specialty and absolutely delicious. I have recreated her recipe to make the prep and cook time a little more doable for an everyday meal. REBECCA

Serves *4* / ***Prep*** *15 minutes* / ***Cook*** *30 minutes*

- 1 teaspoon olive oil
- ½ teaspoon yellow mustard seeds
- 20 fresh curry leaves
- 1 brown onion, chopped
- 1 tablespoon finely grated fresh ginger
- 2 garlic cloves, crushed
- ½ teaspoon ground cumin
- ½ teaspoon ground coriander
- 3 teaspoons ground turmeric
- 4 cardamom pods, lightly crushed
- 1 cinnamon stick
- 1 tablespoon (10 g) coconut milk powder
- 810 g can crushed tomatoes
- 1 tablespoon (20 ml) lime juice
- 4 x 160 g skinless salmon fillets
- 1½ cups (300 g) brown rice
- Lime wedges, to serve
- 1 tablespoon chopped fresh coriander

1. Heat oil in a large, deep non-stick frying pan over medium-high heat. Cook mustard seeds and curry leaves, stirring, until the seeds start to pop. Add onion, ginger and garlic and cook, stirring, for 5 minutes. Add cumin, ground coriander, 2 teaspoons turmeric, cardamom, cinnamon and coconut milk powder and cook, stirring, for a further 1 minute or until fragrant. Stir in tomatoes and lime juice. Season with salt and pepper. Reduce heat, gently simmer for 10 minutes.

2. Add salmon fillets to curry sauce, cover and simmer for a further 12 minutes or until salmon is cooked through.

3. Meanwhile, cook rice following packet instructions, adding remaining turmeric to the cooking water.

4. Serve curry with rice and lime wedges. Sprinkle with coriander.

- **TO REFRIGERATE:** Make curry sauce (step 1) up to 5 days ahead and store in a large reusable container. To serve, bring curry sauce to a simmer in a large, deep frying pan and continue with steps 2–4.
- **TO FREEZE:** Store curry sauce as above for up to 3 months. Thaw at room temperature and complete recipe as above.

Rebecca's tip

This recipe can be made with any type of fish fillets. If using white fish, reduce the cooking time in step 2 to 8–10 minutes, until fish is cooked through.

See page 9 for details

Slow-cooker *osso buco*

7 PersonalPoints per serve

An Italian dish that is satisfying and just a little luxurious. It's ideal to make ahead of time as it tastes amazing on the second day, but it's equally as perfect to dig out of the freezer when you're in the mood for a hearty meal.

WENDY

Serves *6* / ***Prep*** *15 minutes* / ***Cook*** *5 hours 20 minutes – 9 hours 20 minutes*

- 1.5 kg bone-in veal osso buco
- 40 g plain flour
- 1 teaspoon reduced-fat oil spread
- 1 large brown onion, finely chopped
- 1 large carrot, finely chopped
- 2 celery sticks, finely chopped
- 2 large garlic cloves, crushed
- 1 cup (250 ml) red wine
- 400 g can diced tomatoes
- 1 beef stock cube, crumbled
- 2 dried bay leaves
- 3 teaspoons finely chopped fresh thyme

GREMOLATA

- 2 tablespoons finely chopped fresh flat-leaf parsley
- 1 large garlic clove, crushed
- 1 teaspoon finely grated lemon zest

1. Dust both sides of the osso buco with flour. Melt oil spread in a large non-stick frying pan over medium–high heat. Cook osso buco in 2 batches for about 3 minutes on each side or until browned, then transfer to a 5.5 litre (22 cup) capacity slow cooker.
2. Add onion, carrot, celery, garlic and a splash of water to the same frying pan. Cook over medium heat, stirring occasionally, for about 5 minutes or until softened slightly. Transfer vegetables and any crusty bits from the base of the pan to slow cooker with wine, tomatoes, stock cube, bay leaves and thyme. Season with salt and pepper and stir well. Cover with lid and cook on high for 5 hours (or low for 9 hours).
3. To make gremolata, combine all ingredients in a small bowl.
4. Sprinkle gremolata over osso buco to serve.

- **TO REFRIGERATE:** Transfer osso buco to a large reusable container or divide individual portions into separate reusable containers. Store for up to 4 days. To reheat, simmer gently in a saucepan or microwave single servings until hot, stirring in a little water if sauce is too thick.
- **TO FREEZE:** Store osso buco as above for up to 3 months. Thaw overnight in the fridge. Reheat as above.

Wendy's tip

I like to serve my osso buco on cauliflower mash for a ZeroPoint side.

See page 9 for details

‘Bottom of the fridge’ *pasta bake*

3-10 **PersonalPoints range per serve** 

One of the best ways to use up all the veggies at the bottom of the fridge is to throw them all together into a pasta bake. My family looks forward to the ‘old’ veggies for this very reason. Comforting pasta packed full of veggie goodness with a cheesy top . . . what’s not to love?

REBECCA

Serves 4 / *Prep* 15 minutes / *Cook* 45 minutes

250 g wholemeal spiral pasta
500 g turkey breast mince
4 cups (600 g) chopped fresh vegetables (see tip)
400 g can diced tomatoes
2 tablespoons chopped fresh flat-leaf parsley
2 tablespoons chopped fresh chives
100 g grated mozzarella cheese

1 Cook pasta in a large saucepan of boiling salted water, following packet instructions, or until al dente. Drain and set aside.

2 Meanwhile, heat a large saucepan over medium-high heat. Cook mince, stirring to break up lumps, for about 5 minutes or until no longer pink. Add chopped vegetables, tomatoes, half the parsley and half the chives. Cook, stirring occasionally, for about 10 minutes or until vegetables have softened slightly. Stir in cooked pasta. Season with salt and pepper.

3 Transfer mixture to a large baking dish or casserole dish and top with mozzarella. Bake at 180°C for 20–30 minutes or until golden brown. Sprinkle with remaining parsley and chives.

- TO REFRIGERATE: Store unbaked pasta bake, covered, in baking dish, for up to 2 days. When ready to serve, uncover and bake, increasing cooking time by 5 minutes or until hot in the centre.
- TO FREEZE: Check the baking dish is freezer-safe, then store as above for up to 2 months. Thaw overnight in the fridge. Bake as above.

Rebecca’s tip

Use whatever ZeroPoint veggies you have in the bottom of the fridge. I used capsicum, zucchini, carrot, onion and mushrooms. You can also use frozen vegetables instead of fresh, if you prefer.

See page 9 for details

Cauli rice nasi goreng with prawns

2-5 **PersonalPoints range per serve** 

Growing up, I always loved takeaway meals, especially Asian ones as this was my dad's preference. We didn't have them very often, so when we did it was always special. This recipe is a lightened-up version of those fondly remembered childhood meals.

REBECCA

Serves 4 / *Prep* 20 minutes / *Cook* 10 minutes

1 cauliflower, coarsely chopped
2 carrots, cut into 1 cm pieces
2 zucchini, cut into 1 cm pieces
1 brown onion, chopped
200 g broccoli, finely chopped
1 garlic clove, crushed
2 cm piece of ginger, very finely sliced
¼ teaspoon sesame oil
2 teaspoons soy sauce or tamari
2 teaspoons fish sauce
350 g cooked peeled prawns, tails intact
4 eggs
2 tablespoons (35 g) fried shallots
⅓ cup fresh coriander leaves

1 Process cauliflower in a large food processor until it resembles rice.

2 Heat a large non-stick wok over high heat. Stir-fry carrots, zucchini, onion, broccoli, garlic and ginger with sesame oil, soy and fish sauces and a splash of water for 3–5 minutes, until vegetables are just tender. Add cauliflower rice and prawns to wok. Season with salt and pepper. Stir-fry for a further 2 minutes or until cauliflower has softened and prawns are heated through.

3 Meanwhile, lightly spray a large non-stick frying pan with oil and heat over medium heat. Crack eggs into pan and cook until whites are set but yolks are still runny.

4 Divide cauli rice among 4 bowls. Top each serving with an egg. Sprinkle with fried shallots and coriander.

- TO REFRIGERATE: Store cauli rice (without prawns and eggs) in a large reusable container for up to 2 days. To reheat, stir-fry with a splash of water in a wok over medium–high heat until hot. Add prawns and stir-fry for a further minute. Cook eggs following instructions in step 3.

- TO FREEZE: Store cauli rice (without prawns and eggs) as above for up to 2 months. Thaw overnight in the fridge. Reheat as above.

See page 9 for details

Cheat's seafood marinara *pizza*

8-15 PersonalPoints range per pizza

Friday night in my house equals fakeaway night, which is generally pizza on the couch. My favourite variety is a fiery seafood number, loaded with lots of chilli and zesty lemon. I keep Lebanese bread in the freezer for nights like this. It's the perfect quick cook for an evening in.

REBECCA

Makes *1* / ***Prep*** *10 minutes* / ***Cook*** *25 minutes*

- 300 g fresh or frozen seafood marinara mix
- 1 x 80 g wholemeal Lebanese bread
- 1 tablespoon (20 ml) reduced-sugar barbecue sauce
- ¼ red onion, thinly sliced
- 1 teaspoon dried chilli flakes
- 2 tablespoons (20 g) grated mozzarella cheese
- 3 cooked peeled tiger prawns, tails intact
- 1 teaspoon finely shredded lemon zest
- 2 teaspoons chopped fresh flat-leaf parsley
- Lemon wedges, to serve

1 Preheat oven to 200°C.

2 Heat a large non-stick frying pan over medium-high heat. Cook marinara mix, stirring, for 3-4 minutes, until seafood is just cooked. Remove from heat.

3 Place bread on a baking tray and spread with barbecue sauce, then top with marinara mix, onion, chilli and mozzarella. Bake for 15-20 minutes, until cheese is golden.

4 Top pizza with prawns and sprinkle with lemon zest and parsley. Serve with lemon wedges.

See page 9 for details

Sicilian chicken

5-7 PersonalPoints range per serve 

This Sicilian-inspired chicken dish is sure to become your next family favourite. Juicy chicken, cooked in a rich tomatoey sauce with crunchy, toasted pine nuts – it's simply too good to pass up.

WENDY

Serves 4 / *Prep* 15 minutes / *Cook* 35 minutes

- 4 x 150 g skinless chicken breasts
- 1 red onion, sliced
- 3 garlic cloves, crushed
- 1 small fresh red chilli, halved, deseeded
- 3 dried bay leaves
- 250 g cherry tomatoes
- 60 g pine nuts, toasted
- ½ cup (125 ml) red wine
- 200 ml salt-reduced chicken stock
- ⅓ cup (80 ml) balsamic vinegar
- 1 tablespoon (20 ml) sugar-free maple syrup
- ⅓ cup fresh basil leaves

1 Season both sides of chicken with salt and pepper. Lightly spray a large non-stick frying pan with oil and heat over medium-high heat. Cook chicken breasts for 2–3 minutes on each side, until golden brown.

2 Add onion, garlic, chilli, bay leaves, tomatoes and half the pine nuts to pan. Stir in wine and stock. Bring to the boil, then reduce heat and simmer for 20 minutes. Stir in vinegar and maple syrup. Simmer gently for a further 10 minutes. Remove from heat and top with remaining pine nuts and basil leaves to serve.

- **TO REFRIGERATE:** Transfer Sicilian chicken to a large reusable container or divide individual portions into separate reusable containers. Store for up to 2 days. To reheat, simmer gently in a frying pan or microwave single servings until hot, stirring in a little water if sauce is too thick.
- **TO FREEZE:** Store Sicilian chicken as above. Thaw overnight in the fridge. Reheat as above.

Wendy's tip

Serve with a leafy garden salad to increase the veggie count and add some freshness on the side.

See page 9 for details

Wendy's DIY curry night

Growing up in South Africa, curry was a staple in our household. Takeaway curries and their delicious partner in crime, naan, can easily take up a chunk of your PersonalPoints Budget. Here I show you my PersonalPoints-friendly recipes that taste amazing and will save you money too.

My go-to chicken curry (page 122)

My *go-to* chicken curry

0–3 **PersonalPoints range per serve** 

Curries are on high rotation in my household. My freezer is always stocked with homemade curry, especially this one. If you prefer a more subtle heat, use mild curry powder. I love to add extra chilli when serving . . . for me, the spicier the better!

WENDY

***Serves** 4 / **Prep** 15 minutes / **Cook** 1 hour 10 minutes*

1 large brown onion, chopped
3 garlic cloves, crushed
1 teaspoon finely grated fresh ginger
2 teaspoons hot curry powder
1 teaspoon ground turmeric
1 teaspoon garam masala
1 teaspoon cumin seeds
1 teaspoon ground cinnamon
3 cardamom pods, lightly bruised
600 g skinless chicken breasts, cut into 4 cm pieces
400 g can diced tomatoes
1 tablespoon (15 g) monk fruit sweetener
½ cup chopped fresh coriander, plus extra sprigs to serve

1 Lightly spray a large non-stick saucepan with oil and heat over medium–low heat. Cook onion, garlic, ginger and all the spices, stirring, for 3–4 minutes, until onion has softened slightly. Add a little water to prevent spices burning, if necessary.

2 Add chicken to pan and stir well to coat with spices. Stir in tomatoes and season with salt. Cover and simmer gently for 1 hour or until chicken is tender, stirring occasionally and adding a little more water if the sauce starts to look dry. Stir in sweetener in the last 5 minutes of cooking time.

3 Remove from heat. Remove cardamom pods and stir in chopped coriander. Stand, covered, for 5 minutes. Scatter over extra coriander sprigs to serve.

- **TO REFRIGERATE:** Transfer curry to a large reusable container or divide individual portions into separate reusable containers. Store for up to 2 days. To reheat, simmer gently in a saucepan or microwave single servings until hot, stirring in a little water if curry is too thick.

- **TO FREEZE:** Store curry as above for up to 3 months. Thaw overnight in the fridge. Reheat as above.

See page 9 for details

Garlic not-butter

My garlic not-butter is a low PersonalPoints alternative to garlic butter. It can be added to flavour veggies, roast meat and pastas, and used to make garlic bread. The possibilities are endless.

WENDY

Serves 20 / Prep 10 minutes

100 g reduced-fat oil spread
20 garlic cloves (see tip)
2 tablespoons chopped fresh flat-leaf parsley

1 Process all ingredients in a food processor until well combined. Transfer to a reusable container.

- **TO REFRIGERATE:** Store not-butter in a reusable container for up to 2 weeks.
- **TO FREEZE:** Store not-butter in a reusable container for up to 2 months or freeze individual portions in covered silicone ice-cube trays.

Wendy's tips

- My family and I are big garlic lovers. If you're not, use 10–15 garlic cloves instead.
- This recipe makes about 1½–2 teaspoons per serve.

See page 9 for details

Easy garlic naan

4-5 PersonalPoints range per naan

Soft, fluffy and delicious, this homemade naan is an easy two-ingredient dough with added spice and garlic. These are great to have on hand in the freezer to serve with curries. Not to mention you're saving a tonne of PersonalPoints (and money!) by not buying the takeaway versions.

WENDY

Makes *4* / ***Prep*** *10 minutes* / ***Cook*** *20 minutes*

1 cup (150 g) self-raising flour
¼ teaspoon ground cumin
1 teaspoon garlic salt
3 garlic cloves, crushed
150 g 99% fat-free plain yoghurt

1. Place flour, cumin, garlic salt and garlic in a medium bowl. Stir in yoghurt with a flat-blade knife to form a dough. Turn dough onto a lightly floured surface and knead for 1–2 minutes, until smooth. Divide dough into 4 even portions. Shape each portion into a ball and roll out to a 15 cm round.

2. Lightly spray a non-stick frying pan with oil and heat over medium heat. Cook naan, 1 at a time, for 2–3 minutes on each side, until evenly browned and cooked through.

- **TO REFRIGERATE:** Store cooked naans in a reusable snap-lock bag for up to 2 days. Microwave until warm to serve.

- **TO FREEZE:** Store cooked naans as above for up to 3 months. Reheat as above.

Wendy's tips

- Instead of spraying the frying pan with oil you can line it with a WW non-stick liner.
- For an extra hit of garlic, spread naan with 1 teaspoon of my Garlic not-butter (page 123) before serving.

See page 9 for details

Spiced coriander & lemon rice

5 **PersonalPoints per serve** 

Perfect served with my chicken curry, this fragrant rice is a quick side dish that is bursting with flavour and a great way to use up leftovers. Pack it in your freezer alongside my chicken curry (page 122) and naan (opposite) for a quick Indian fakeaway evening.

WENDY

Serves 4 / *Prep* 10 minutes / *Cook* 10 minutes

- 1 brown onion, finely chopped
- 3 garlic cloves, crushed
- 1 teaspoon finely grated fresh ginger
- 1 long fresh green chilli, finely chopped (optional)
- 1 dried bay leaf
- 1 teaspoon cumin seeds
- 2 teaspoons ground turmeric
- 2 cups (340 g) cooked jasmine rice (hot)
- 1 cup chopped fresh coriander
- 1 tablespoon (20 ml) lemon juice

1 Lightly spray a large non-stick frying pan with oil and heat over medium heat. Cook onion, stirring, for 5 minutes or until soft. Add garlic, ginger, chilli, bay leaf and cumin seeds. Cook, stirring, for a further 1–2 minutes, until fragrant. Add a splash of water if mixture starts to catch on the base of pan.

2 Remove from heat and stir in turmeric. Add rice, coriander and lemon juice. Stir until well combined and season with salt. Serve hot or cold (after being refrigerated following the instructions below).

- **TO REFRIGERATE:** Store spiced rice in a reusable container for up to 2 days.
- **TO FREEZE:** Divide individual portions into reusable snap-lock bags. Remove as much air as possible from bags, then seal and flatten bags. Stack on top of each other and store for up to 1 month. Thaw in the fridge or microwave from frozen until hot.

Wendy's tip

Use a packet of microwave jasmine rice if you don't have time to cook rice from scratch. Just be sure to check the PersonalPoints in the WW app.

See page 9 for details

Tuscan beef & lentil *stew*

2-5 **PersonalPoints range per serve** 

Don't you love it when a throw-together 'made up on the spot with the stuff in the fridge' meal just works? This is exactly what happened when I first cooked my Tuscan beef and lentil stew. Any combination of veggies, fresh or frozen, can work here – just give it a go with what you have on hand. Plus, it tastes even better the next day, so cook up extra to store in the fridge or freezer.

REBECCA

Serves 4 / *Prep* 20 minutes / *Cook* 4–7 hours

450 g lean gravy beef steaks, fat trimmed, cut into 2 cm pieces
1 cup (200 g) dried red lentils
1 brown onion, chopped
2 garlic cloves, crushed
2 zucchini, chopped
2 carrots, chopped
2 celery sticks, chopped
400 g can diced tomatoes
2 tablespoons (45 g) tomato paste
2 teaspoons Tuscan seasoning
2 teaspoons beef stock powder
¼ cup chopped fresh flat-leaf parsley

1 Place all ingredients, except parsley, in a 5.5 litre (22 cup) capacity slow cooker. Stir in 1 litre (4 cups) water. Cook on low for 6–7 hours (or high for 4 hours), until beef is very tender. Season with salt and pepper.

2 Scatter over parsley to serve.

- **TO REFRIGERATE:** Transfer stew to a large reusable container or divide individual portions into separate reusable containers. Store for up to 2 days. To reheat, simmer gently in a saucepan or microwave single servings until hot, stirring in a little water if stew is too thick.

- **TO FREEZE:** Store stew as above. Thaw overnight in the fridge. Reheat as above.

See page 9 for details

Easy prosciutto-wrapped chicken

5-8 **PersonalPoints range per serve** 

One of the first 'grown up' meals I cooked when I moved out of home was this oh-so-easy prosciutto-wrapped chicken. It sounds impressive, but don't be fooled! It's so easy to make and tastes amazing. To save time, I make the rolls up to 2 days in advance and store them, wrapped tightly in their foil casings, in the fridge.

REBECCA

Serves *4* / ***Prep*** *20 minutes* / ***Cook*** *40 minutes*

4 x 200 g skinless chicken breasts
16 slices (200 g) prosciutto, fat trimmed
4 x 16 g light cream cheese wedges

1 Preheat oven to 180°C. Place a chicken breast between 2 pieces of plastic wrap (see tip). Using a rolling pin or flat meat mallet, gently pound chicken to an even thickness (about 5 mm thick). Repeat with remaining chicken breasts.

2 Lay 4 slices of prosciutto on a piece of baking paper, overlapping slightly along the long edges. Place a chicken breast on the prosciutto at the short edge. Spread a wedge of cheese over chicken, then roll up chicken in prosciutto from the short edge to form a sausage shape. Wrap tightly in the baking paper, twist ends to form a bon bon shape, then wrap completely in foil. Repeat with remaining chicken, prosciutto and cheese to make 4 in total. Place on a baking tray.

3 Bake for 35 minutes. Remove from oven, carefully remove foil and baking paper. Heat a large non-stick frying pan over medium heat. Sear prosciutto and chicken rolls in pan for about 5 minutes, turning occasionally, until prosciutto is crisp and golden.

- **TO REFRIGERATE:** Prepare chicken to the end of step 2 up to 2 days ahead. Cook as required, following instructions in step 3.
- **TO FREEZE:** Prepare chicken to the end of step 2. Place wrapped rolls in a reusable container or large snap-lock bag and store for up to 2 months. Thaw overnight in the fridge. Transfer to a baking tray and cook following instructions in step 3.

Rebecca's tips

- I used Laughing Cow light cheese wedges, but any light cream cheese will work.
- You can recycle soft plastics at major supermarkets. Look for the recycling bin by the checkouts.

See page 9 for details

Mince curry & *egg pie* (babotie)

A traditional South African dish, babotie consists of a curry-flavoured minced meat, topped off with an egg and milk-based layer. It is a dish very near to my heart – my mother taught me to make it. Babotie beautifully demonstrates the fusion of cultures in South Africa, with a colourful and fragrant result.

WENDY

Serves *8* / ***Prep*** *20 minutes* / ***Cook*** *1 hour 15 minutes*

- **1 cup (250 ml) skim milk**
- **2 x 35 g slices white bread**
- **1 brown onion, finely chopped**
- **3 garlic cloves, crushed**
- **800 g extra-lean beef mince**
- **¼ cup (40 g) raisins**
- **1 tablespoon (20 g) apricot jam**
- **1 tablespoon (25 g) fruit chutney**
- **2 teaspoons curry powder**
- **1 teaspoon ground turmeric**
- **1 tablespoon (15 g) monk fruit sweetener**
- **5 dried bay leaves**
- **1 large egg**

1. Preheat oven to 180°C. Lightly spray a rectangular ovenproof dish (about 23 cm x 33 cm x 5 cm deep) with oil.
2. Pour milk over bread in a shallow dish. Set aside until bread absorbs milk. Squeeze excess milk from the bread. Set aside milk and bread in separate bowls.
3. Heat a large non-stick saucepan over medium heat. Cook onion and garlic, stirring, for 2–3 minutes, until softened. Add mince and cook, stirring to break up lumps, until browned. Crumble soaked bread into the pan and stir well. Stir in raisins, jam, chutney, curry powder, turmeric, sweetener and 2 bay leaves. Season with salt and pepper. Spoon into the prepared dish and bake for 45 minutes. Remove from oven.
4. Add egg and a pinch of salt to the reserved milk and whisk well. Gently pour the egg mixture over the mince mixture in dish and place the remaining 3 bay leaves on top. Return to the oven for 25 minutes. Serve.

- **TO REFRIGERATE:** Store cooked babotie, covered in ovenproof dish, for up to 3 days. Reheat individual portions in microwave.
- **TO FREEZE:** Check the ovenproof dish is freezer-safe, then store as above for up to 2 months. Thaw in fridge and reheat as above.

Wendy's tips

- **Any flavour of fruit chutney will work a delight here. Some of my favourites include mango, peach or fig.**
- **If raisins aren't your thing, swap for medjool dates or leave out completely.**

See page 9 for details

Dad's slow-braised beef (trinchado)

5 PersonalPoints per serve

Trinchado is a traditional South African braised beef dish with strong Portuguese influences in its origin. I like to make a double batch so there is one quantity to serve straight away and another to freeze for later use. Not a fan of chilli and olives? No worries – leave them out.

WENDY

Serves 4 / Prep 15 minutes + marinating / Cook 1 hour

- 400 g lean beef rump steak, fat trimmed, cut into 4 cm pieces
- 5 garlic cloves, finely chopped
- 200 ml red wine
- 1 large brown onion, finely chopped
- 1 tablespoon (10 g) plain flour
- 2 beef stock cubes, crumbled
- 1 teaspoon dried chilli flakes
- 2 dried bay leaves
- 50 g kalamata olives

1 Combine beef, garlic and wine in a large bowl. Cover and marinate in the fridge for 30 minutes.

2 Lightly spray a large saucepan with oil and heat over medium heat. Cook onion, stirring occasionally, for about 8 minutes or until soft. Using a large slotted spoon, remove meat from the marinade and add to the pan (reserve remaining marinade). Sprinkle over flour and cook over medium-high heat, stirring, for about 5 minutes or until meat is evenly browned.

3 Stir in stock cubes, chilli, bay leaves, reserved marinade and 300 ml water until well combined. Cover and simmer, stirring occasionally, for about 45 minutes or until meat is tender and sauce has thickened. Remove from heat. Stir in olives and season with salt. Serve.

- TO REFRIGERATE: Transfer trinchado to a large reusable container or divide individual portions into separate reusable containers. Store for up to 2 days. To reheat, simmer gently in a saucepan or microwave single servings until hot, stirring in a little water if sauce is too thick.
- TO FREEZE: Store trinchado as above. Thaw overnight in the fridge. Reheat as above.

Wendy's tips

- Serve trinchado with steamed green vegetables and parsley to boost the veg.
- While most of the alcohol is cooked off during the braising process, you can use alcohol-free wine if you like.

See page 9 for details

Greek lamb meatballs with zoodles

My nana's family was Greek-Australian, so lamb meatballs were always a favourite when she babysat me and my younger brother. I used to sit on the bench and roll the meatballs with her, then watch as she fried them in lots of oil. I've lightened up her original recipe by removing the oil and replacing the pasta with zoodles.

REBECCA

Serves 4 / *Prep* 30 minutes / *Cook* 45 minutes

500 g lean lamb mince
1 teaspoon garlic powder
1 teaspoon onion powder
1 teaspoon dried oregano
1 teaspoon ground nutmeg
1 tablespoon chopped fresh chives, plus extra to serve
1 teaspoon finely grated lemon zest
4 zucchini, spiralised

SAUCE
1 brown onion, finely chopped
1 garlic clove, crushed
2 carrots, grated
1 zucchini, grated
800 g can diced tomatoes
2 teaspoons chicken stock powder
2 tablespoons (45 g) tomato paste
400 g can lentils, drained and rinsed
⅓ cup (55 g) pitted kalamata olives, chopped

1. Place mince, garlic powder, onion powder, oregano, nutmeg, chives and lemon zest in a large bowl. Season with salt and pepper and mix until well combined. Roll tablespoons of mixture into balls.

2. Heat a large non-stick frying pan over medium-high heat. Cook meatballs, turning occasionally, until browned all over. Remove meatballs and set aside. Reserve any juices remaining in the pan.

3. To make sauce, heat the same pan over medium-high heat. Cook onion and garlic for 2-3 minutes, stirring, until onion is lightly browned. Add carrot and grated zucchini and cook, stirring, for a further 3 minutes or until softened. Stir in remaining ingredients. Season with salt and pepper. Bring to the boil.

4. Return meatballs to the pan and gently stir to coat in sauce. Reduce heat to low and simmer, covered, for 30 minutes.

5. Cook spiralised zucchini (zoodles) in a large saucepan of boiling water for 1 minute, then drain. Serve meatballs and sauce over zoodles. Sprinkle with extra chives.

- **TO REFRIGERATE:** Transfer meatballs and sauce to a large reusable container or divide individual portions into separate reusable containers. Store for up to 2 days. To reheat, simmer gently in a frying pan or microwave single servings until hot, stirring in a little water if too thick. Cook zoodles just before serving.

- **TO FREEZE:** Store meatball and sauce as above. Thaw overnight in the fridge. Reheat as above. Cook zoodles just before serving.

See page 9 for details

Curried chicken drumsticks with rice

7-13 **PersonalPoints range per serve** 

This fab one-pot recipe is one I've been making forever. It was shared with me by my very first WW Coach over 20 years ago. I've made a few tweaks and changes over the years to get it just the way I like it.

REBECCA

Serves 4 / *Prep* 15 minutes / *Cook* 45 minutes

- 12 x 125 g chicken drumsticks, skin removed
- 3 teaspoons curry powder
- 1 teaspoon garlic-infused olive oil
- 1 brown onion, finely chopped
- 2 carrots, cut into 1 cm pieces
- 5 whole cup mushrooms, cut into 1 cm pieces
- 2 teaspoons finely grated fresh ginger
- 1 cup (145 g) frozen peas
- 1 cup (200 g) brown basmati rice
- 1 teaspoon chicken stock powder
- ¼ cup chopped fresh flat-leaf parsley

1. Preheat oven to 200°C.
2. Heat a large non-stick ovenproof frying pan over medium-high heat. Cook chicken, turning occasionally, for about 5 minutes or until browned all over. Sprinkle over curry powder and cook, turning for a further 1-2 minutes, until fragrant. Transfer chicken to a plate.
3. Add oil, onion, carrot and mushrooms to the pan and cook, stirring, for about 5 minutes or until vegetables have softened slightly. Add ginger, peas, rice and stock powder and cook, stirring, for a further minute. Remove from heat.
4. Return chicken to the pan and stir in 2 cups (500 ml) hot water. Season with salt and pepper. Cover with an ovenproof lid or foil. Carefully transfer pan to oven. Bake for 30 minutes or until chicken is cooked through and liquid is absorbed. Scatter parsley over top to serve.

- **TO REFRIGERATE:** Transfer individual portions to reusable containers and store for up to 2 days. Reheat in microwave.

Rebecca's tip

If you don't have an ovenproof frying pan, complete steps 1-3 in a frying pan, then transfer mixture to a large baking dish and continue with step 4.

See page 9 for details

Slow-cooked beef cheek lasagne

8-9 **PersonalPoints range per serve** 

What's better than lasagne? Seven-hour slow-cooked beef cheek lasagne! This is a real bells and whistles of the classic Italian dish. Just turn on the slow cooker and let it do the work for you.

WENDY

Serves 6 / *Prep* 15 minutes / *Cook* 8 hours 40 minutes

- 900 g lean beef cheeks, fat trimmed
- 1 brown onion, finely chopped
- 3 garlic cloves, crushed
- 3 teaspoons dried thyme
- 400 g can diced tomatoes
- 140 g fresh lasagne sheets
- 1 cup (80 g) grated parmesan cheese

WHITE SAUCE

- 200 g 99% fat-free plain Greek yoghurt
- 2 egg yolks
- ¼ teaspoon ground nutmeg

1. Lightly spray a 5.5 litre (22 cup) capacity slow cooker with oil. Add beef cheeks and onion. Cover with lid and cook on high for 4 hours.

2. Turn beef cheeks and add garlic and thyme. Season with salt and pepper. Cover with lid and cook on low for a further 3 hours or until meat is very tender. Use two forks to coarsely shred meat in the slow cooker. Stir in tomatoes. Cover with lid and cook on high for a further 1 hour.

3. Meanwhile, to prepare white sauce, whisk yoghurt, egg yolks and nutmeg in a jug until well combined. Season with salt and pepper and set aside.

4. Preheat oven to 180°C.

5. Spread half the beef mixture over base of a large rectangular ovenproof dish. Cover with lasagne sheets. Spread remaining beef mixture over lasagne sheets, then pour over white sauce and sprinkle with parmesan cheese. Cover with foil and bake for 20 minutes. Remove foil and return to oven for 15–20 minutes, until top is golden brown.

- **TO REFRIGERATE:** Store prepared lasagne (with unbaked top), covered with foil, for up to 2 days. Bake as required, increasing cooking time by 5–10 minutes.

See page 9 for details

Chicken goulash *with pasta*

3-8 **PersonalPoints range per serve** 

This recipe came out of a craving for comforting pasta smothered in a delish goulash sauce. Not your typical culinary partners, but somehow it just works!

REBECCA

Serves *4* / ***Prep*** *20 minutes* / ***Cook*** *40 minutes*

1 tablespoon (20 g) reduced-fat oil spread
600 g skinless chicken breast, cut into thin strips
1 brown onion, thinly sliced
2 garlic cloves, crushed
250 g whole cup mushrooms, sliced
1 red capsicum, cut into thin strips
2 celery sticks, sliced
1 tablespoon smoked paprika
2 teaspoons chicken stock powder
400 g can diced tomatoes
1 cup (260 g) tomato passata
150 g wholemeal pasta
250 g packet frozen spinach, thawed
¼ cup (60 ml) light sour cream
¼ teaspoon dried chilli flakes

1. Melt oil spread in a large saucepan over medium-high heat. Cook chicken, turning occasionally, for 3–4 minutes, until no longer pink.

2. Add onion, garlic, mushrooms, capsicum and celery to pan. Cook, stirring, for 5–7 minutes, until vegetables have softened slightly. Add paprika and stock powder. Cook, stirring, for a further 1 minute.

3. Stir in tomatoes and passata and bring to the boil. Season with salt and pepper. Reduce heat and simmer, covered, for 30 minutes.

4. Meanwhile, cook pasta in a large saucepan of boiling salted water, following packet instructions, or until al dente. Drain.

5. Stir spinach and sour cream through the chicken mixture. Sprinkle with chilli flakes. Serve with pasta.

- **TO REFRIGERATE:** Transfer goulash to a large reusable container or divide individual portions into separate reusable containers. Store for up to 2 days. To reheat, simmer gently in a saucepan or microwave single servings until hot, stirring in a little water if goulash is too thick. Cook pasta just before serving.

- **TO FREEZE:** Store goulash as above. Thaw overnight in the fridge. Reheat as above.

See page 9 for details

Chicken, noodle & corn *egg drop* soup

3-8 PersonalPoints range per serve 

When I make this soup I am instantly five years old again, sitting in the back of the car and carefully holding my Chinese takeaway chicken and corn soup as Dad drives home. The flavours take me right back . . .

REBECCA

Serves *4* / ***Prep*** *15 minutes* / ***Cook*** *20 minutes*

1 brown onion, finely chopped
500 g skinless chicken breast, thinly sliced
2 garlic cloves, crushed
2 teaspoons finely grated fresh ginger
2 cups (320 g) fresh or frozen corn kernels
1 tablespoon (20 g) chicken stock powder
90 g angel hair pasta, broken into 5–6 cm lengths
1 green shallot (spring onion), thinly sliced
3 eggs, lightly beaten
1 tablespoon finely chopped fresh chives

1. Lightly spray a large non-stick saucepan with oil and heat over medium heat. Cook onion, stirring, for 3 minutes or until softened. Add chicken, garlic and ginger and cook, stirring, for 5 minutes or until chicken is no longer pink.

2. Stir in corn, stock powder and 1.5 litres (6 cups) boiling water and bring to the boil. Reduce heat and simmer, covered, for 5 minutes. Stir in pasta and shallot and simmer, uncovered, for a further 4–5 minutes, until pasta is al dente.

3. Remove saucepan from heat. Pour in egg in a steady stream, stirring constantly. Season with salt and pepper. Sprinkle with chives to serve.

- **TO REFRIGERATE:** Transfer soup to a large reusable container or divide individual portions into separate reusable containers. Store for up to 2 days. Reheat in a saucepan over low heat, stirring occasionally, or microwave single servings until hot.

- **TO FREEZE:** Store soup as above. Thaw overnight in the fridge. Reheat as above.

See page 9 for details

Pork *fried* rice

5–13 PersonalPoints range per serve 

There are so many recipes for fried rice, with endless combinations of flavours. My pork fried rice recipe is a really great way to add extra veg into your day (and sneak it in for the kids too!). I always cook a double batch, and freeze half of it in single serves, ready to grab and heat up for a quick lunch or dinner option.

REBECCA

Serves 4 / *Prep* 20 minutes / *Cook* 30 minutes

- 1 teaspoon olive oil
- 1 brown onion, finely chopped
- 2 garlic cloves, crushed
- 1 tablespoon finely grated fresh ginger
- 1 teaspoon chilli paste
- 500 g lean pork mince
- 1 zucchini, cut into 1 cm pieces
- 1 carrot, cut into 1 cm pieces
- 4 whole cup mushrooms, cut into 1 cm pieces
- ¼ teaspoon Chinese five spice
- 1 tablespoon (20 ml) soy sauce
- 1 tablespoon (20 ml) fish sauce
- 1 tablespoon (20 ml) oyster sauce
- 4 cups (680 g) cooked brown rice (see tip)
- 1 cup (145 g) frozen peas, thawed

1 Heat oil in a large non-stick wok or frying pan over medium heat. Add onion, garlic, ginger and chilli paste and cook, stirring, for 2–3 minutes, until onion is softened slightly. Add mince and cook, stirring to break up lumps, for about 5 minutes or until no longer pink.

3 Add zucchini, carrot, mushrooms, spice and sauces to wok. Season with ground white pepper and stir-fry for 2 minutes or until well combined. Reduce heat to low, cover and cook for 5 minutes. Stir through rice and peas, cover and cook for a further 5 minutes or until heated through.

- **TO REFRIGERATE:** Divide individual portions of fried rice into reusable containers. Store for up to 2 days. To serve, reheat in microwave until hot.
- **TO FREEZE:** Store fried rice as above. Thaw overnight in the fridge. Reheat as above.

Rebecca's tip

Day-old rice works best for fried rice, as much of the moisture dries out of the grains, helping to give them the perfect texture for frying.

See page 9 for details

Beef & feta patties (page 145)

Quinoa & black bean patties (page 144)

Wendy's perfect patties

I've always got a variety of patties in my freezer for emergencies. While delicious eaten on their own with a side of salad and veggies, they're also great to enjoy as a juicy burger or in my Deconstructed burger bowl (page 92). You can personalise the flavours to meet your own taste buds, or follow my recipes for inspiration.

Curried chicken patties (page 145)

WENDY

Quinoa & black bean patties

1-4 **PersonalPoints range per patty** 

Packed with flavour and seriously satisfying, add these tasty, fibre-filled patties to your weekly rotation if you're keen to include some meat-free days in your meal plan.

***Makes** 4 / **Prep** 10 minutes / **Cook** 15 minutes*

¼ cup (45 g) quinoa
400 g can black beans, drained and rinsed
1 egg, lightly beaten
½ cup (35 g) dried breadcrumbs
2 tablespoons chopped fresh coriander
½ teaspoon smoked paprika
½ teaspoon ground cumin
1 teaspoon garlic salt

1 Combine quinoa and ½ cup (125 ml) water in a small saucepan and bring to the boil. Reduce heat, cover and simmer for about 15 minutes or until water has been absorbed.

2 Meanwhile, mash beans in a bowl with a fork. Add cooked quinoa and remaining ingredients. Mix until well combined. Divide mixture into 4 even portions. Shape into patties.

3 Lightly spray a large non-stick frying pan with oil (or line with a WW non-stick liner) and heat over medium heat. Cook patties for about 3 minutes each side or until evenly browned.

- **TO REFRIGERATE:** Prepare patties up to 2 days ahead. Store in a reusable container and cook as required. Cooked patties will keep in a reusable container for up to 5 days.

- **TO FREEZE:** Store cooked patties as above, with baking paper between each patty, for up to 2 months. Thaw at room temperature.

See page 9 for details

Curried *chicken* patties

 **0-2 PersonalPoints range per patty**  

Homemade curried chicken burgers are just . . . the best! The Indian spices are a tasty addition to a regular burger patty. I buy chicken breasts and blitz them in a food processor to make my own mince: that way I know it will be zero PersonalPoints for me.

Makes 4 / Prep 10 minutes / Cook 10 minutes

400 g chicken breast mince
1 teaspoon finely grated fresh ginger
1 teaspoon ground cumin
1 teaspoon curry powder
1 small fresh red chilli, finely chopped
3 garlic cloves, crushed
½ cup chopped fresh coriander (leaves and stems)

1 Place all the ingredients in a bowl and season with salt and pepper. Mix until well combined. Divide mixture into 4 even portions. Shape into patties.

2 Lightly spray a large non-stick frying pan with oil (or line with a WW non-stick liner) and heat over medium heat. Cook patties for 5–6 minutes on each side, until cooked through.

- **TO REFRIGERATE:** Store cooked patties in a reusable container for up to 3 days.
- **TO FREEZE:** Store cooked patties as above, with baking paper between each patty, for up to 2 months. Thaw overnight in the fridge.

See page 9 for details

Beef & feta patties

 **4 PersonalPoints per patty**  

Why order a takeaway when you can enjoy these succulent homemade patties in just 20 minutes? This recipe is a must-make for your next cook-up. I often swap out the feta for blue cheese, but use whatever cheese you prefer.

Makes 4 / Prep 10 minutes / Cook 10 minutes

400 g extra-lean beef mince
60 g reduced-fat feta cheese, finely crumbled
1 garlic clove, crushed
1 teaspoon dried rosemary

1 Place all ingredients in a medium bowl and season with salt and pepper. Mix until well combined. Divide mixture into 4 even portions. Shape into patties.

2 Lightly spray a large non-stick frying pan with oil (or line with a WW non-stick liner) and heat over medium heat. Cook patties for 4–5 minutes on each side, until cooked through.

- **TO REFRIGERATE:** Store cooked patties in a reusable container for up to 3 days.
- **TO FREEZE:** Store cooked patties as above, with baking paper between each patty, for up to 2 months. Thaw overnight in the fridge.

See page 9 for details

Shake-n-bake chicken on pumpkin smash

6 PersonalPoints per serve

This recipe was created on a cold and overcast day, when I REALLY wanted comfort food. Instead of opting for the hot chips and gravy the kids were begging me to buy, I decided to use what I had in the fridge and pantry and came up with this beautiful, warming meal.

REBECCA

Serves 4 / Prep 20 minutes / Cook 40 minutes

- ¼ cup (40 g) plain flour
- 2 teaspoons smoked paprika, plus extra to serve
- 1 teaspoon dried Italian herbs
- 8 x 125 g chicken drumsticks, skin removed
- 800 g butternut pumpkin, peeled, chopped
- 2 teaspoons butter

1 Preheat oven to 180°C. Line a baking tray with baking paper.

2 Combine flour, paprika, herbs and chicken in a large reusable snap-lock bag. Seal bag and shake to coat chicken. Transfer chicken to prepared tray. Lightly spray with oil and bake for 35–40 minutes, until golden and cooked through.

3 Meanwhile, to make pumpkin smash, place pumpkin in a microwave-safe dish, cover and microwave on High (100%) for about 6 minutes or until soft. Season with salt and pepper, add butter and coarsely mash with a fork.

4 Serve chicken on pumpkin smash. Sprinkle lightly with extra paprika.

- **TO REFRIGERATE:** Transfer individual portions of chicken and pumpkin smash to reusable containers. Store for up to 2 days. To serve, reheat in microwave until hot.
- **TO FREEZE:** Store cooked pumpkin smash in a reusable container for up to 3 months. Defrost in fridge, then cook chicken as per recipe.

Rebecca's tips

- For an extra serve of veggies, add some ZeroPoint greens on the side, such as steamed broccoli, beans or zucchini.
- For a shortcut, replace chicken drumsticks with 8 chicken lovely legs.

See page 9 for details

Lamb *bolognese*

My lamb bolognese packs a big flavour punch and is loaded with fibre, all while cooking in under an hour. It makes 4 really generous serves, so you could easily stretch it out to 6 meals and pop the leftovers in the freezer.

REBECCA

Serves 4 / *Prep* 15 minutes / *Cook* 40 minutes

- 1 brown onion, finely chopped
- 2 garlic cloves, crushed
- 500 g lean lamb mince
- 2 carrots, grated
- 2 zucchini, grated
- 400 g can diced tomatoes
- 400 g can lentils, drained and rinsed
- 1 teaspoon beef stock powder
- ¼ teaspoon mixed dried herbs
- 250 g wholemeal spaghetti
- 2 tablespoons (15 g) grated parmesan cheese
- 1 tablespoon chopped fresh flat-leaf parsley

1. Heat a large saucepan over medium heat. Cook onion and garlic, stirring, for 2–3 minutes, until softened slightly. Add mince and cook, stirring to break up lumps, until browned.
2. Stir in carrot, zucchini, tomatoes, lentils, stock powder and herbs. Season with salt and pepper. Bring to the boil, then reduce heat and simmer, partially covered, for 20–30 minutes, stirring occasionally, until sauce has thickened.
3. Meanwhile, cook spaghetti in a large saucepan of boiling, salted water, following packet instructions, or until al dente. Drain.
4. Serve spaghetti and bolognese sauce topped with parmesan and parsley.

- **TO REFRIGERATE:** Transfer bolognese sauce to a large reusable container or divide individual portions into separate reusable containers. Store for up to 4 days. To reheat, simmer gently in a saucepan or microwave single servings until hot, stirring in a little water if sauce is too thick. Cook pasta just before serving.
- **TO FREEZE:** Store bolognese sauce as above. Thaw overnight in the fridge. Reheat as above.

See page 9 for details

Pork *lasagne cups*

6 PersonalPoints per cup

The easiest pork lasagne that you will ever make, conveniently made into single-serve portions. Perfect for meals on the go and kid-approved too!

WENDY

Makes *6* / ***Prep*** *20 minutes* / ***Cook*** *20 minutes*

3 x 34 g dried lasagne sheets
½ brown onion, finely chopped
450 g lean pork mince
1 garlic clove, finely chopped
100 ml reduced-sugar tomato sauce
1 teaspoon dried thyme
150 g 99% fat-free plain yoghurt
1 egg yolk
½ cup (60 g) grated mozzarella

1 Preheat oven to 200°C.

2 Cook lasagne sheets in a saucepan of boiling water for 10 minutes, stirring occasionally to prevent sheets sticking together. Drain. Cut lasagne sheets in half. Lightly spray a 6-hole ½ cup (125 ml) capacity muffin tray with oil and place on a baking tray. Line each of the prepared holes with a piece of lasagne to form lasagne cups.

3 Meanwhile, lightly spray a non-stick frying pan with oil and heat over medium heat. Cook onion, stirring, for 5 minutes or until soft. Add mince and cook, stirring to break up lumps, for 5 minutes or until browned. Add garlic, tomato sauce and thyme. Season with salt and cook, stirring, for a further 3 minutes. Fill lasagne cups evenly with mince mixture.

4 Whisk yoghurt and egg yolk in a small bowl until combined. Spoon yoghurt mixture over mince mixture. Sprinkle with mozzarella. Bake for 20 minutes or until golden brown.

- **TO REFRIGERATE:** Store cooked lasagne cups in a reusable container for up to 2 days. Reheat in microwave.
- **TO FREEZE:** Place each cooked lasagne cup in a reusable snap-lock bag and store for up to 3 months. Thaw overnight in the fridge. Reheat as above.

Wendy's tips

- You can use wonton wrappers instead of lasagne sheets, if you prefer.
- Serve with a fresh salad of baby rocket, cherry tomatoes and cucumber.

See page 9 for details

Chicken *stir-fry* with chilli, basil and cashews

3–5 **PersonalPoints range per serve** 

Nothing screams quick and easy like a stir-fry! Chilli and basil marry perfectly together, and the cashews add a delicious toasty crunch. It does take a little prep time for the marinade to work its magic (totally worth it!) but the rest is done in just 30 minutes.

REBECCA

Serves 4 / Prep 20 minutes + marinating / Cook 10 minutes

- 600 g skinless chicken breasts, cut into thin strips
- 1 tablespoon (20 ml) teriyaki sauce
- 2 garlic cloves, crushed
- 2 teaspoons finely grated fresh ginger
- 2 teaspoons olive oil
- 1 brown onion, thinly sliced
- 2 carrots, cut into 1 cm thick batons
- 1 red capsicum, cut into 1 cm thick strips
- 1 zucchini, sliced
- 5 yellow button squash, sliced
- 5 whole cup mushrooms, sliced
- 1 tablespoon (20 ml) soy sauce
- 1 tablespoon (20 ml) fish sauce
- 1 tablespoon (20 ml) light sweet chilli sauce
- 1 tablespoon finely shredded fresh basil leaves, plus extra to serve
- 2 green shallots (spring onions), thinly sliced
- ¼ cup (40 g) unsalted cashews

1. Combine chicken, teriyaki sauce, garlic and ginger in a bowl. Toss well. Cover and marinate in the fridge for several hours or overnight.
2. Heat 1 teaspoon oil in a large non-stick wok over high heat. Stir-fry marinated chicken in batches for 2–3 minutes, until lightly browned and just cooked through. Remove from wok and set aside.
3. Heat remaining oil in same wok over medium-high heat. Stir-fry onion and carrot with a splash of water for 2 minutes. Add capsicum, zucchini, squash and mushrooms and stir-fry for a further 2–3 minutes, until vegetables are just tender.
4. Return chicken to the wok with sauces and basil. Season with salt and pepper. Stir-fry until well combined and heated through. Top with extra basil leaves, shallots and cashews to serve.

- **TO REFRIGERATE:** Divide individual portions of stir fry into reusable containers and store for up to 3 days. To serve, reheat in microwave until hot.

See page 9 for details

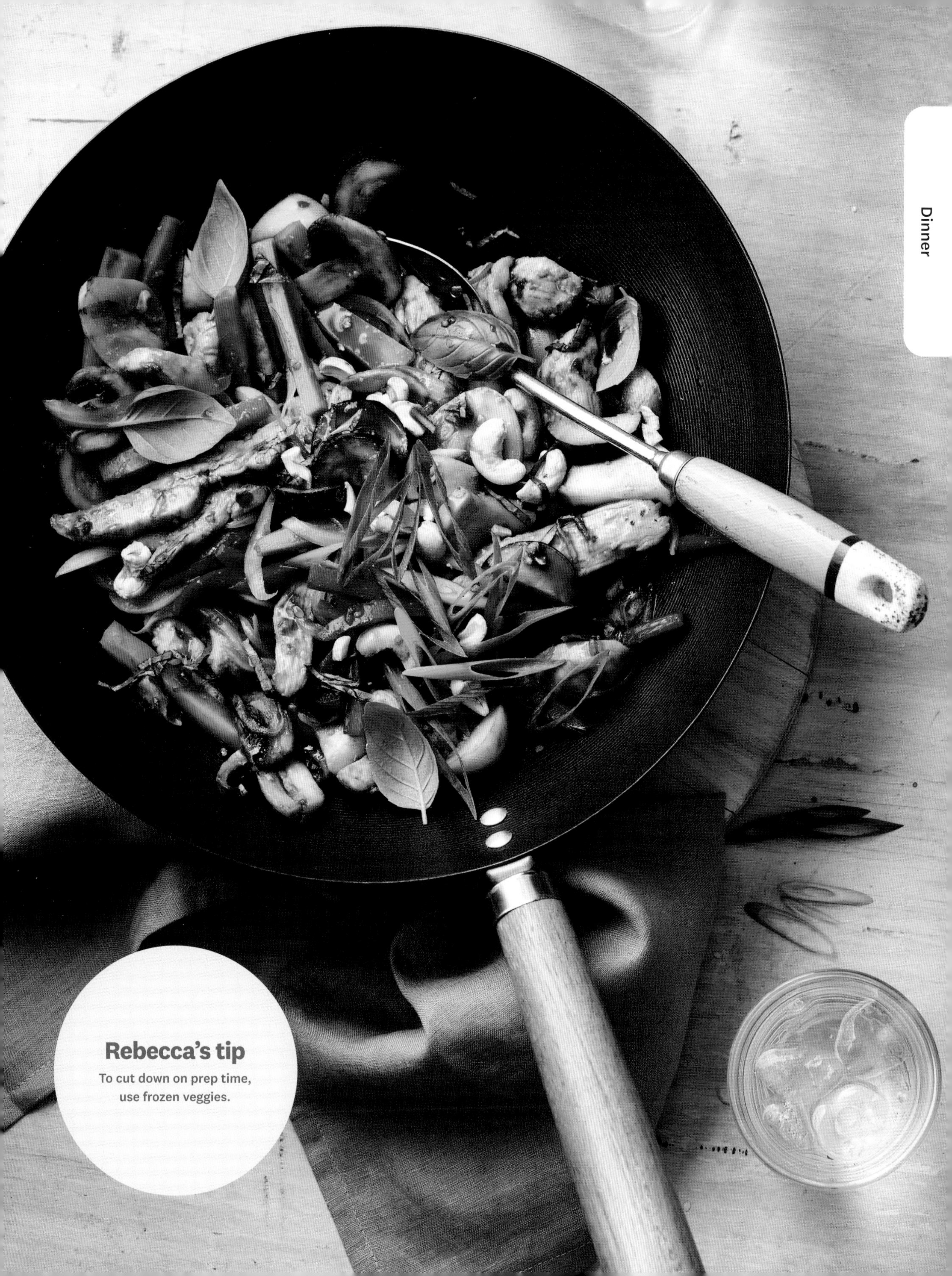

Rebecca's tip

To cut down on prep time, use frozen veggies.

Slow-cooker red lentil & sweet potato curry

2-6 **PersonalPoints range per serve** 

Meal-prepping is so easy when you put your slow cooker to work. This recipe makes 8 portions, so stocking your freezer with 'I can't be bothered' dinners is a breeze. All it takes is 15 minutes of prep in the morning. REBECCA

Serves 8 / *Prep* 15 minutes / *Cook* 3 hours 45 minutes – 7 hours 30 minutes

2 brown onions, finely chopped
2 garlic cloves, crushed
1 tablespoon finely grated fresh ginger
1 teaspoon ground cumin
1 teaspoon ground coriander
1 teaspoon curry powder
1 teaspoon garam masala
1 teaspoon vegetable stock powder
50 g coconut milk powder
2 cups (400 g) dried red lentils
250 g cauliflower, cut into 2 cm pieces
250 g orange sweet potato (kumara), cut into 2 cm pieces
1 zucchini, cut into 2 cm pieces
400 g can diced tomatoes
400 g can chickpeas, drained and rinsed
150 g baby spinach leaves
1 cup fresh coriander sprigs

1 Place all ingredients, except for chickpeas, spinach and coriander sprigs in a 5.5 litre (22 cup) slow cooker. Add 1 litre (4 cups) water and stir to combine. Cook on high for 3.5 hours (or low for 7 hours).

2 Stir in chickpeas and spinach. Season with salt and pepper. Cook on high for a further 15 minutes (or low for 30 minutes). Top with coriander sprigs to serve.

Stove-top method:

1 Heat a large non-stick saucepan over medium heat. Cook onion, garlic and ginger, stirring, for 2–3 minutes, until softened slightly. Add spices and stock powder and cook, stirring, for a further 1 minute.

2 Stir in coconut milk powder, lentils, cauliflower, sweet potato, zucchini and tomatoes. Add enough water to cover vegetables. Bring to the boil, then reduce heat and simmer for 30–40 minutes, until vegetables and lentils are tender, stirring occasionally and adding extra water if mixture starts to catch on base of pan.

3 Stir in chickpeas and spinach. Season with salt and pepper. Simmer for a further 5 minutes. Top with coriander sprigs.

- **TO REFRIGERATE:** Transfer curry to a large reusable container or divide individual portions into separate reusable containers. Store for up to 5 days. To reheat, simmer gently in a saucepan or microwave single servings until hot, stirring in a little water if curry is too thick.

- **TO FREEZE:** Store curry as above. Thaw overnight in the fridge. Reheat as above.

See page 9 for details

Maple-glazed salmon with watermelon & feta salad

Salmon is perfect when you want a quick and hearty meal. I always have some in my freezer – I transfer it to the fridge in the morning and cook it up for dinner. The watermelon and feta salad is the ideal quick pairing for a refreshing meal, especially when the weather is a little warmer.

WENDY

Serves 2 / *Prep* 10 minutes / *Cook* 6 minutes

- 2 x 125 g skinless salmon fillets
- 2 tablespoons (40 ml) sugar-free maple syrup

WATERMELON & FETA SALAD

- 200 g watermelon, rind removed
- 50 g reduced-fat feta cheese, thinly sliced
- ½ red onion, thinly sliced
- 8 pitted kalamata olives, halved
- ½ teaspoon dried chilli flakes
- ¼ cup fresh mint leaves
- 2 teaspoons lime juice

1. Season salmon with salt and pepper. Lightly spray a non-stick frying pan with oil (or line with a WW non-stick liner) and heat over medium heat. Cook salmon for 3 minutes, then turn and cook the other side for 2 minutes. Drizzle over maple syrup, cook for a further 1 minute or until cooked to your liking.

2. Meanwhile, to make salad, cut watermelon into small triangles. Divide watermelon, feta and onion between 2 serving plates. Scatter over olives, chilli flakes and mint leaves. Drizzle with lime juice. Serve with salmon.

- **TO REFRIGERATE:** Cook salmon up to 1 day ahead and store in a reusable container. Prepare salad up to 2 hours ahead. Keep covered in a separate container. Remove salmon and salad from the fridge when ready to eat and enjoy cold.

See page 9 for details

Spanish rice

7-12 **PersonalPoints range per serve**   

I really love rice dishes, and paella is one of my favourites. Unfortunately, when cooked in the traditional way, paella is a little too time-consuming for a midweek meal. My Spanish rice recipe cooks in half the time, and is perfect to freeze in individual portions.

REBECCA

Serves 4 / *Prep* 20 minutes / *Cook* 20 minutes

- 1 cup (200 g) brown rice
- ¼ teaspoon saffron threads
- 250 g chorizo sausage, cut into 1 cm pieces
- 1 red onion, chopped
- 2 garlic cloves, crushed
- 2 tomatoes, chopped
- 2 zucchini, chopped
- 1 cup (145 g) frozen peas
- 200 g whole cup mushrooms, sliced
- ½ cup (80 g) drained canned corn kernels
- 1 red capsicum, chopped
- 2 teaspoons smoked paprika
- 2 tablespoons chopped fresh flat-leaf parsley
- 1 lime, cut into wedges

1. Cook rice following packet instructions. Combine saffron with 1 tablespoon boiling water in a small heatproof bowl. Stand for 5 minutes.

2. Meanwhile, heat a large, deep non-stick frying pan over medium heat. Cook chorizo for 3–4 minutes, stirring, until crisp and lightly browned. Add onion and garlic and cook, stirring, for a further 2 minutes. Stir in tomatoes, zucchini, peas, mushrooms, corn, capsicum and paprika. Cook, stirring occasionally, for 10 minutes or until vegetables are tender. Season with salt and pepper.

3. Add cooked rice, saffron water and 1 tablespoon parsley to pan. Stir to combine and cook until rice is heated through. Sprinkle with remaining parsley and serve with lime wedges.

- **TO REFRIGERATE:** Divide individual portions of Spanish rice into reusable containers and store for up to 3 days. To serve, reheat in microwave until hot.
- **TO FREEZE:** Store Spanish rice as above for up to 3 months. Reheat as above.

See page 9 for details

Paprika *chicken* nuggets

2-5 PersonalPoints range per serve 

When my kids were little, my homemade chicken nuggets were known as MFC – Mum's Fried Chicken – and they were the most requested kids' dinner. Unbeknown to them, however, the nuggets are baked and come in at a fraction of the PersonalPoints value of their deep-fried takeaway counterparts. Still, according to my kids, they are 'better than KFC'!

REBECCA

Serves 4 / *Prep* 20 minutes + marinating / *Cook* 30 minutes

¾ cup (180 g) 99% fat-free plain Greek yoghurt
1 garlic clove, crushed
1 teaspoon smoked paprika
600 g skinless chicken breast, cut into 2 cm pieces
50 g panko breadcrumbs
1 teaspoon garlic salt
Baby rocket leaves, to serve
Lemon wedges, to serve

1 Mix yoghurt, garlic, half the paprika and ¼ cup (60 ml) water in a large bowl. Add chicken and stir to coat in yoghurt mixture. Cover and refrigerate for at least 2 hours or overnight (see tip).

2 Preheat oven to 180°C. Combine breadcrumbs, garlic salt and remaining paprika in a large snap-lock bag. Season with salt and pepper.

3 Drain and discard excess yoghurt from chicken. Add chicken to crumb mixture in bag. Seal the bag and shake well to coat chicken in the crumbs.

4 Line a large baking tray with baking paper. Place a wire rack over the prepared tray and lightly spray with oil. Arrange chicken pieces on the rack in a single layer. Lightly spray again with oil. Bake for 25–30 minutes, turning halfway through cooking time, until golden and cooked through. Serve with rocket and lemon wedges.

- TO REFRIGERATE: Store cooked nuggets in a reusable container for up to 2 days. Serve cold or reheat in the oven, microwave or air fryer until hot.

Rebecca's tips

- Marinating the chicken overnight will make for super tender nuggets.
- For extra flavour, use garlic oil spray on chicken in step 4 instead of regular oil spray.

See page 9 for details

Snacks

Sweet orange bread

Inspiration for this sweet bread hit when I was making 2-ingredient dough for scrolls (see pages 179–80). A beautiful friend gave me a bag of oranges and the scent was so fragrant I knew I had to find a way to combine the zest with the yoghurt-based dough. This is the result! REBECCA

Serves 8 / *Prep* 20 minutes / *Cook* 40 minutes

- 1 cup (240 g) 99% fat-free plain yoghurt
- ½ cup (110 g) monk fruit sweetener
- 1 teaspoon vanilla bean paste
- 1 tablespoon finely grated orange zest
- ¼ cup (60 ml) freshly squeezed orange juice
- 1¼ cups (190 g) self-raising flour
- 1 teaspoon baking powder

TOPPING

- ½ cup (110 g) monk fruit sweetener
- 2 teaspoons finely grated orange zest
- ½ teaspoon vanilla bean paste
- 2 tablespoons (40 ml) skim milk, approximately
- 4 orange slices

1. Preheat oven to 170°C.
2. Whisk yoghurt, sweetener and vanilla in a bowl until creamy and well combined. Stir in orange zest and juice.
3. Sift flour, baking powder and a pinch of salt into a large bowl. Add yoghurt mixture and use a flat-blade knife to cut and fold through until just combined (do not overmix).
4. Pour mixture into a lightly oiled and baking paper-lined 12 cm x 22 cm loaf tin (or a WW silicone loaf tin). Bake for 35–40 minutes, until cooked in the centre when tested with a skewer. Stand in tin for 5 minutes, then turn out onto wire rack to cool completely.
5. To make topping, place sweetener, orange zest and vanilla in a bowl. Stir in enough milk to give a grainy, spreadable consistency. Spread over the top of loaf. Decorate with orange slices. Cut into 8 slices to serve.

- TO REFRIGERATE: Store topped loaf in a reusable container for up to 5 days.
- TO FREEZE: Store plain loaf (without topping) as above for up to 2 months. Thaw at room temperature. Prepare topping and spread over loaf just before serving.

Rebecca's tip

If you prefer a smoother icing rather than a crunchy top, blend the sweetener in a food processor, add a little extra milk and stir until the sweetener is completely dissolved.

See page 9 for details

Garlic seafood crispbread 'pizzas' (page 168)

Mushroom crispbread 'pizzas' (page 169)

Nutty date & banana crispbreads (page 169)

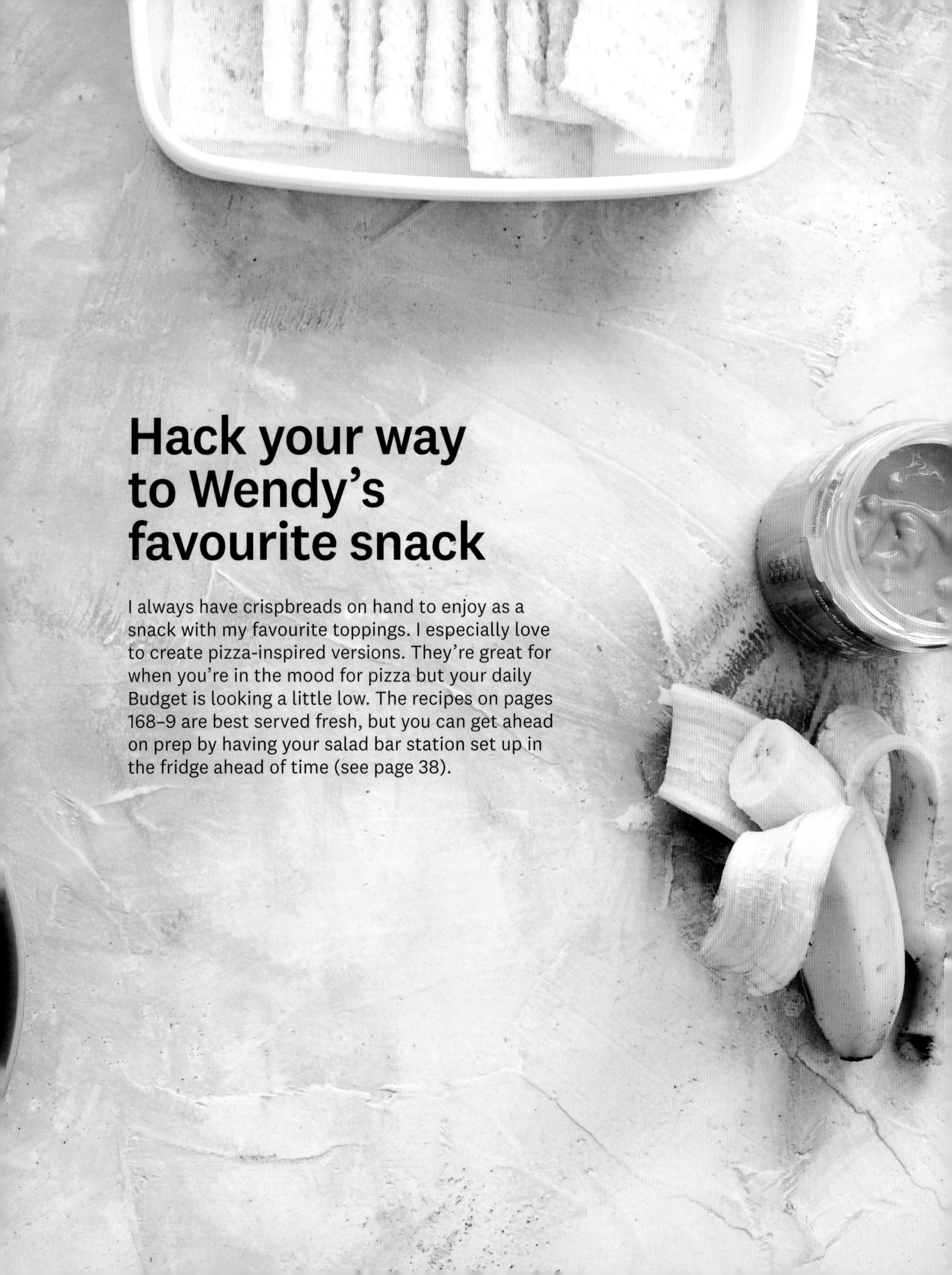

Hack your way to Wendy's favourite snack

I always have crispbreads on hand to enjoy as a snack with my favourite toppings. I especially love to create pizza-inspired versions. They're great for when you're in the mood for pizza but your daily Budget is looking a little low. The recipes on pages 168–9 are best served fresh, but you can get ahead on prep by having your salad bar station set up in the fridge ahead of time (see page 38).

WENDY

Garlic *seafood* crispbread 'pizzas'

3-6 **PersonalPoints range per serve** 

Seafood pizza has to be my all-time favourite pizza. Juicy prawns and canned tuna topped with melted mozzarella cheese delivers a high protein snack or light meal, ready in just 10 minutes.

Serves *1* / *Prep* *5 minutes* / *Cook* *5 minutes*

- 2 x 6 g light puffed crispbreads
- 1 teaspoon tomato paste
- 95 g can tuna in springwater, drained
- ¼ small red onion, finely chopped
- 4 cooked king prawns, peeled, deveined, tails intact
- ¼ teaspoon dried mixed herbs
- 2 tablespoons (20 g) grated mozzarella cheese
- 1 small garlic clove, finely chopped
- 2 teaspoons chopped fresh flat-leaf parsley

1 Spread crispbreads with tomato paste. Top evenly with tuna, onion and prawns. Sprinkle with dried herbs and mozzarella.

2 Cook in an air fryer at 180°C for 4–5 minutes or under a preheated grill, until cheese is melted and light golden. Top with garlic and parsley. Season with salt and pepper.

Wendy's tips

- I use Cruskits as they're very low in PersonalPoints, but you can use any crispbread you prefer.
- If you don't like raw garlic, sprinkle it over the tomato paste in step 1 instead.

See page 9 for details

Mushroom crispbread 'pizzas'

3 PersonalPoints per serve

A great vegetarian 'pizza' option. You could also add a little goat's cheese if you're a fan.

***Serves** 1 / **Prep** 5 minutes / **Cook** 5 minutes*

2 x 6 g light puffed crispbreads
1 teaspoon tomato paste
2 large whole cup mushrooms, sliced
2 tablespoons (20 g) grated mozzarella cheese
1 teaspoon fresh flat-leaf parsley, finely chopped

1 Spread crispbreads with tomato paste. Top evenly with mushrooms and mozzarella. Season with salt and pepper. Cook in an air fryer at 180°C for 4–5 minutes or under a preheated grill, until cheese is melted and light golden. Sprinkle with parsley just before serving.

See page 9 for details

Nutty date & banana crispbreads

4–8 PersonalPoints range per serve

Banana, peanut butter and dates unite for a sweet and healthy snack that's sure to satisfy your taste buds.

***Serves** 1 / **Prep** 5 minutes*

2 x 6 g light puffed crispbreads
2 teaspoons natural peanut butter (100% nuts)
½ small banana, sliced
2 medjool dates, pitted and chopped
1 teaspoon sugar-free maple syrup

1 Spread crispbreads with peanut butter. Top 1 crispbread with banana and the other crispbread with dates. Drizzle with maple syrup.

See page 9 for details

3-ingredient *beer bread*

5 PersonalPoints per serve 

A South African favourite, this is a clever way to make a quick loaf. You don't need to add yeast, as the yeast in the beer helps the bread-making process. My recipe uses just 3 ingredients, but you can easily add other flavours. Try ham and cheese, or olives and sun-dried tomatoes.

WENDY

***Serves** 8 / **Prep** 10 minutes / **Cook** 45 minutes*

2 cups (300 g) self-raising flour
1½ teaspoons dried thyme or mixed herbs
350 ml can beer

1 Preheat oven to 180°C. Lightly spray a 12 cm x 22 cm loaf tin (or a WW silicone loaf tin) with oil.

2 Sift flour and ½ teaspoon salt into a large mixing bowl. Stir in dried herbs and beer, adding a little water if the mixture is too dry. Spoon mixture into prepared tin. Bake for 40–45 minutes, until top is golden brown and a skewer inserted in the centre comes out clean. Stand loaf in tin for 10 minutes before turning out and cutting into 8 slices to serve.

- TO STORE: Keep bread in a reusable container at room temperature for up to 3 days.
- TO FREEZE: Store individual slices in reusable snap-lock bags for up to 3 months. Toast frozen slices or microwave until warm to serve.

See page 9 for details

Choc-nut *energy* bliss bites

1-2 **PersonalPoints range per serve** 

I love the idea of bliss balls, but it's the thought of rolling the mixture that I just can't be bothered with. Instead, I make up the mixture and pop it into a tray to set, then simply cut it into bite-sized pieces. All the deliciousness of a bliss ball, without the fuss of rolling – winning!

REBECCA

***Serves** 32 / **Prep** 15 minutes + soaking*

- **½ cup (80 g) almonds**
- **½ cup (50 g) walnuts**
- **½ cup (75 g) unsalted cashews**
- **¼ cup (25 g) cocoa powder**
- **1 cup (230 g) medjool dates, pitted and chopped**

1. Place nuts in a bowl and cover with cold water. Soak overnight. Drain.
2. Lightly spray a 16 cm x 26 cm slice tin with oil and line base and sides with baking paper.
3. Transfer drained nuts to a food processor. Add cocoa and dates and process until well combined (add a little water if necessary to help the mixture come together). Spread mixture evenly into prepared tin. Cover and place in freezer for at least 2 hours, until firm.
4. Lift slice from tin using baking paper. Stand for about 10 minutes to soften slightly, then cut into 32 pieces. Transfer pieces to a reusable container and store in freezer. Thaw pieces for a few minutes to soften slightly before eating.

- TO FREEZE: Store bliss bites in a reusable container for up to 4 months. Thaw at room temperature for 5 minutes before serving.

See page 9 for details

High-fibre banana loaves

The classic banana bread with a healthy, high-fibre makeover. Easy to make and perfect for brunch, snacking or breakfast on the go.

WENDY

Makes 6 / *Prep* 10 minutes / *Cook* 25 minutes

- 2 bananas, mashed, plus ½ banana, thinly sliced
- 100 g wheat bran cereal, finely crushed
- 1 teaspoon baking powder
- 3 medjool dates, pitted and finely chopped
- 2 eggs, lightly beaten
- 1 teaspoon vanilla essence
- 1½ tablespoons (30 ml) sugar-free maple syrup (optional)

1 Preheat oven to 180°C. Lightly spray a 6-hole ¾ cup (180 ml) capacity mini loaf mould tray with oil (or use 6 silicone mini loaf moulds).

2 Place mashed banana in a large bowl. Add cereal, baking powder, dates, eggs and vanilla. Mix until well combined.

3 Spoon mixture evenly into prepared moulds and top with banana slices (see storage tip). Bake for 20–25 minutes, until a skewer inserted in the centre of loaves comes out clean. Stand in tray for 10 minutes before turning out onto a wire rack to cool.

4 Serve plain or drizzled with syrup.

- TO STORE: Keep loaves in a reusable container at room temperature, without banana topping, for up to 4 days. Top with banana and drizzle with syrup just before serving.

- TO FREEZE: Store loaves in reusable snap-lock bags without toppings, for up to 2 months. To serve, thaw at room temperature or microwave individual frozen loaves until warm. Top with banana and drizzle with syrup just before serving.

Wendy's tip

I used All Bran but you can swap this with crushed Weet-Bix or rolled oats if you prefer.

See page 9 for details

Mini cheese and Vegemite scrolls (see page 178)

Rebecca's rock & scrolls

Two-ingredient dough really is a godsend. It's often used for pizza bases, flatbreads and bagels, but I've enjoyed trying to find new ways to use it, like my Sweet orange bread (page 164) and the ultimate indulgence – scrolls. Sweet or savoury, these little morsels of deliciousness will satisfy cravings any time of the day. It's a really great way to introduce the kids or grandkids to baking, too, as the rolling is so hands-on. You can make the basic dough recipe in advance and either store it in the fridge for up to a week, or freeze it for 2–3 months. Rather than freezing it in a big ball, roll it out and place it in a reusable freezer bag to make the thawing time much faster. Let's rock and scroll!

Apple pie scrolls
(see page 179)

REBECCA

Mini cheese & Vegemite scrolls

3 PersonalPoints per scroll 

Cheese and Vegemite – does it get any more Australian than that? I always have a batch of these in the freezer for school lunch boxes, and for my lunch box, too!

Makes *18* / ***Prep*** *20 minutes* / ***Cook*** *25 minutes*

2 cups (300 g) self-raising flour, plus 1 tablespoon extra for dusting
250 g 99% fat-free plain yoghurt
1 tablespoon (25 g) Vegemite
1 cup (120 g) grated mozzarella cheese

1. Preheat oven to 170°C. Line a baking tray with baking paper.
2. Mix flour and yoghurt in a large bowl to form a dough. Turn dough out onto a bench dusted with the extra flour and knead for 1–2 minutes until smooth.
3. Roll out dough to form a long rectangle, about 20 cm x 70 cm. Place Vegemite in a small heatproof bowl, microwave on High (100%) for 10 seconds, then spread over the dough. Sprinkle evenly with half the mozzarella. Roll up from the long side to form a long roll. Cut into 18 even pieces. Place scrolls, cut-side down, on prepared tray. Flatten slightly so they are just touching each other. Sprinkle with the remaining mozzarella. Bake for 20–25 minutes, until golden and cooked in the centre. Serve warm or at room temperature.

- TO STORE: Keep scrolls in a reusable container, with baking paper between layers, for up to 2 days.
- TO FREEZE: Store scrolls as above for up to 2 months. Thaw at room temperature or microwave until warm.

See page 9 for details

Apple pie scrolls

 **2-3 PersonalPoints range per scroll** 

I created this flavour combo after walking past a bakery . . . okay, I stopped and drooled over the delectable sweet treats in the cabinet window! The apple scrolls caught my eye, so I decided to make my own mini version.

***Makes** 18 / **Prep** 20 minutes / **Cook** 25 minutes*

- 400 g can pie apples (100% apples)
- 2 teaspoons ground nutmeg
- 1 teaspoon brown sugar
- 2 cups (300 g) self-raising flour, plus 1 tablespoon extra for dusting
- 250 g 99% fat-free plain yoghurt
- 1 teaspoon vanilla bean paste
- 3 teaspoons skim milk
- 2 teaspoons icing sugar

1 Preheat oven to 170°C. Line a baking tray with baking paper.

2 Mash the apples with nutmeg and brown sugar in a small bowl.

3 Mix flour, yoghurt and vanilla in a large bowl to form a dough. Turn dough out onto a bench dusted with the extra flour and knead for 1–2 minutes until smooth.

4 Roll out dough to form a long rectangle, about 20 cm x 70 cm. Spread apple mixture over dough. Roll up from the long side to form a long roll. Cut into 18 even pieces. Place scrolls, cut-side down, on prepared tray. Flatten slightly so they are just touching each other. Brush with 2 teaspoons milk. Bake for 20–25 minutes, until golden and cooked in the centre.

5 Meanwhile, to make glaze, mix icing sugar with the remaining milk in a small bowl until combined. Drizzle over scrolls while still warm. Serve warm or at room temperature.

- TO STORE: Keep scrolls in a reusable container, with baking paper between layers, for up to 2 days.
- TO FREEZE: Store scrolls as above for up to 2 months. Thaw at room temperature or microwave until warm.

See page 9 for details

REBECCA

Sticky  scrolls

2-3 PersonalPoints range per scroll

When you have a craving for the sweet deliciousness that only a cinnamon scroll can deliver, this is the recipe for you.

***Makes** 18 / **Prep** 20 minutes + soaking / **Cook** 25 minutes*

12 medjool dates, pitted and chopped
1 teaspoon vanilla bean paste
2 cups (300 g) self-raising flour, plus 1 tablespoon extra for dusting
250 g 99% fat-free plain yoghurt
2 teaspoons ground cinnamon
3 teaspoons skim milk
2 teaspoons icing sugar

1. Place dates in a heatproof bowl. Cover with 1 cup (250 ml) boiling water and set aside to soak for 1 hour.
2. Preheat oven to 170°C. Line a baking tray with baking paper.
3. Drain dates, reserving ½ cup (125 ml) water. Process dates, reserved water, ½ teaspoon vanilla and a pinch of salt in a food processor or blender to form a smooth paste.
4. Mix flour, yoghurt and remaining vanilla in a large bowl to form a dough. Turn dough out onto a bench dusted with the extra flour and knead for 1–2 minutes until smooth.
5. Roll out dough to form a long rectangle, about 20 cm x 70 cm. Spread date paste over dough, then sprinkle with cinnamon. Roll up from the long side to form a long roll. Cut into 18 even pieces. Place scrolls, cut-side down, on prepared tray. Flatten slightly so they are just touching each other. Brush with 2 teaspoons milk. Bake for 20–25 minutes, until golden and cooked in the centre.
6. Meanwhile, to make glaze, mix icing sugar with remaining milk in a small bowl until combined. Drizzle over scrolls while still warm. Serve warm or at room temperature.

- TO STORE: Keep scrolls in a reusable container, with baking paper between layers, for up to 2 days.
- TO FREEZE: Store scrolls as above for up to 2 months. Thaw at room temperature or microwave until warm.

See page 9 for details

Easy oat slice

My friend Malcolm shared this recipe with me. I'm so glad he did as it's become one of my comfort food staples. It also takes just 15 minutes to prepare, so there's no excuse for an empty cookie jar!

WENDY

Serves 20 / Prep 15 minutes / Cook 20 minutes

150 g reduced-fat oil spread
170 g monk fruit sweetener
½ cup (125ml) sugar-free maple syrup
3½ cups (315 g) rolled oats

1 Preheat oven to 180°C. Lightly spray an 18 cm square shallow tin with oil and line base and sides with baking paper.

2 Combine oil spread, sweetener and syrup in a large saucepan over medium heat. Cook, stirring until oil spread has melted and sweetener has dissolved. Remove from heat, add oats and stir until well combined.

3 Press mixture evenly into prepared tin using the back of a large spoon and smooth over the top. Bake for 20 minutes or until golden brown. Remove from oven, cool slightly, then cut into 20 pieces while still in the tin. Cool completely in the tin before removing pieces to serve.

- TO STORE: Keep slices in a reusable container at room temperature for up to 5 days.

See page 9 for details

 scones

3 PersonalPoints per scone 

I have really fond memories of setting up backyard picnics after school with my brother and Granny, and sipping on tea while devouring these scones. This is Granny's original recipe, butter, sugar and all . . . because some things just shouldn't be changed.

REBECCA

Makes 36 / *Prep* 25 minutes / *Cook* 15 minutes

2⅓ cups (350 g) self-raising flour, plus 1 tablespoon extra for dusting
125 g butter, cut into small pieces
1 tablespoon (20 g) caster sugar
¼ cup (40 g) raisins
½ cup (125 ml) skim milk
2 teaspoons raw sugar

1. Preheat oven to 180°C. Line a baking tray with baking paper.
2. Sift flour into a large bowl. Add butter and rub in with your fingertips until mixture resembles breadcrumbs. Stir in sugar and raisins. Using a flat-blade knife, gradually stir in enough milk to form a soft dough (you will need ¼–½ cup).
3. Turn dough out onto a bench dusted with the extra flour. Knead dough very lightly to bring it together, then roll out to a 2 cm thickness. Cut dough into rounds using a 6 cm round cookie cutter. Place rounds close together on prepared tray so they are just touching. Repeat process with dough trimmings until all the dough is used to make 36 scones in total.
4. Lightly brush tops with water, then sprinkle with raw sugar. Bake for 10–15 minutes, until scones are golden. Serve scones warm or transfer to a wire rack to cool.

- TO REFRIGERATE: Store scones in a reusable container for up to 1 week. To reheat, microwave scones until warm, or wrap a batch in foil and place in a 180°C oven for about 10 minutes.
- TO FREEZE: Store scones as above for up to 3 months. Reheat from frozen as above.

Rebecca's tip

Scones are at their best on the day of baking but they also freeze and reheat well.

See page 9 for details

Chocolate-coatec
pistachio dates
(page 186)

Sweet chilli & cream
cheese stuffed dates
(page 187)

Blue cheese-stuffed
dates (page 187)

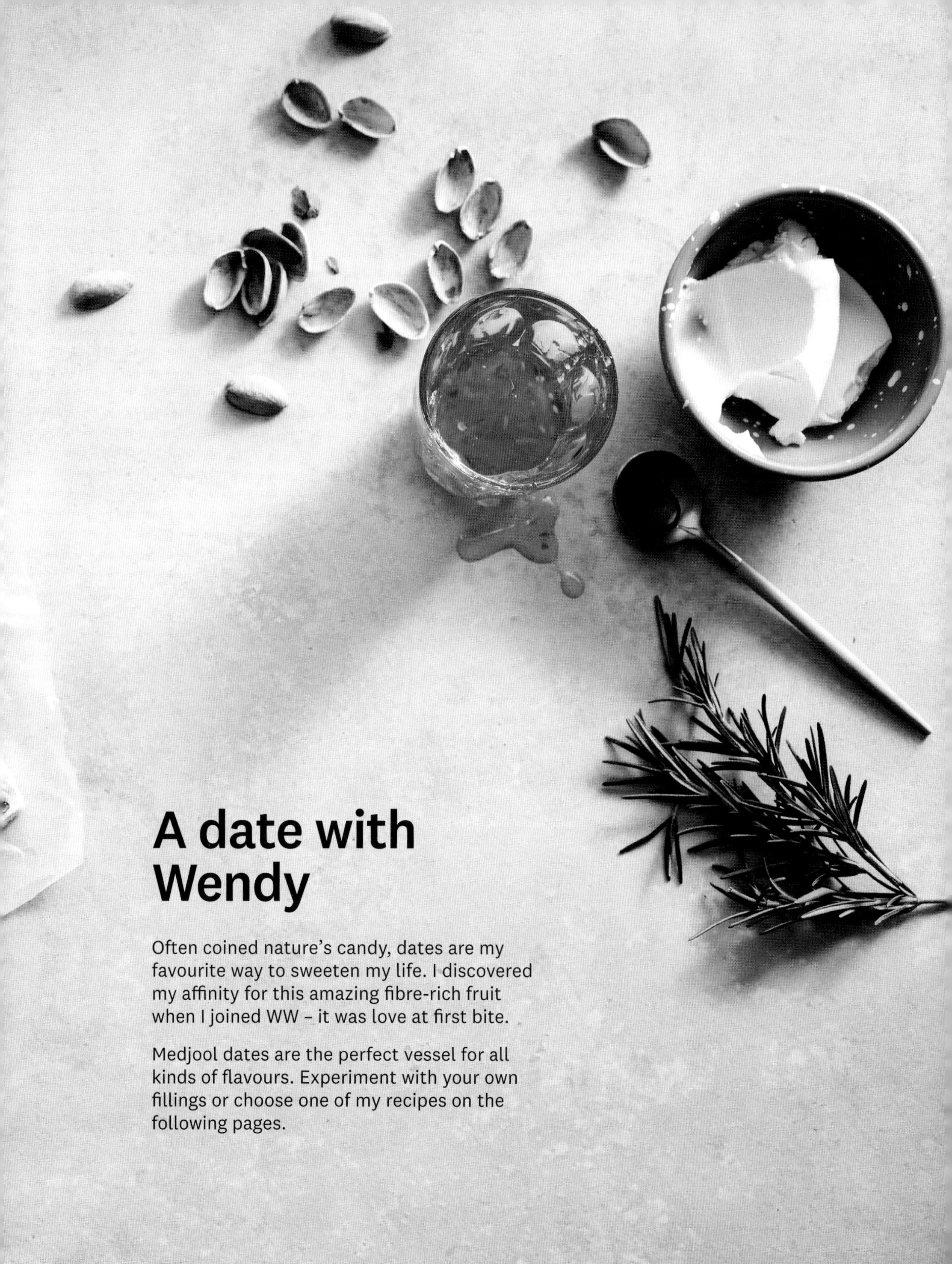

A date with Wendy

Often coined nature's candy, dates are my favourite way to sweeten my life. I discovered my affinity for this amazing fibre-rich fruit when I joined WW – it was love at first bite.

Medjool dates are the perfect vessel for all kinds of flavours. Experiment with your own fillings or choose one of my recipes on the following pages.

WENDY

Chocolate-coated pistachio dates

1-3 **PersonalPoints range per date** 

I love giving these impressive-looking dates as an edible gift to friends and family. Watch as they make a fuss over all the trouble you've gone to, when really you've only spent 15 minutes in the kitchen.

***Makes** 14 / **Prep** 15 minutes*

14 large medjool dates, pitted
14 pistachio kernels
55 g 70% dark chocolate

1 Make an incision lengthways in each date, without cutting right through. Place 1 pistachio in each date.

2 Microwave chocolate in a small microwave-safe bowl in 30-second bursts on High (100%), stirring until smooth and melted.

3 Working quickly, roll dates in melted chocolate to coat, then place on a baking paper-lined tray.

4 Place dates in fridge for 10 minutes or until chocolate is set. Serve.

- TO REFRIGERATE: Store coated dates in a single layer in a reusable container for up to 2 weeks.

- TO FREEZE: Place coated dates in a single layer on a baking tray and freeze for 30 minutes, then transfer to reusable snap-lock bags. Store in freezer for up to 2 months. Thaw in the fridge or at room temperature.

Wendy's tip

Work quickly when rolling the dates to ensure the chocolate doesn't set, or if it does, simply microwave briefly until smooth and melted again.

See page 9 for details

Blue cheese-stuffed dates

Pop these blue-cheese stuffed dates onto a cheeseboard and throw in a bottle of wine – you'll be ready to entertain in minutes!

Makes 14 / *Prep* 10 minutes

14 large medjool dates, pitted
55 g blue cheese, cut into 14 pieces
Fresh rosemary sprigs, to garnish

1 Make an incision lengthways in each date, without cutting right through.

2 Place 1 piece of blue cheese in each date. Garnish with rosemary. Serve.

- TO REFRIGERATE: Store filled dates in a single layer in a reusable container for up to 3 days.

Wendy's tips

- You can eat these fresh or cook in an air fryer at 200°C for 2–3 minutes, until cheese begins to melt.
- Not a fan of blue cheese? Replace with feta or goat's cheese.

See page 9 for details

Sweet chilli & cream cheese stuffed dates

0-2 PersonalPoints range per date

Cream cheese and sweet chilli sauce – a match made in heaven. Add dates to the mix and you've got yourself a deliciously sweet and creamy morsel that's perfect for an afternoon pick-me-up.

Makes 14 / *Prep* 10 minutes

14 large medjool dates, pitted
70 g light cream cheese
1 tablespoon (20 ml) light sweet chilli sauce

1 Make an incision lengthways in each date, without cutting right through.

2 Place 1 teaspoon cream cheese in each date and drizzle with ¼ teaspoon sweet chilli sauce per date. Serve.

- TO REFRIGERATE: Store filled dates, without sweet chilli drizzle, in a single layer in a reusable container for up to 1 day. Drizzle with sweet chilli sauce just before serving.

See page 9 for details

Air-fryer tuna melt bites

1 PersonalPoints per bite

These savoury bites are crispy on the outside, and tender and cheesy on the inside. The perfect protein-rich snack or lunch box staple.

WENDY

Makes 8 / *Prep* 10 minutes / *Cook* 12 minutes

10 g panko breadcrumbs

TUNA MIX
- 185 g can tuna in springwater, drained and flaked
- 1 small red onion, finely chopped
- 1 tablespoon chopped fresh flat-leaf parsley
- 1 garlic clove, crushed
- 1 teaspoon whole grain mustard
- 50 g 99% fat-free plain yoghurt
- ¼ cup (30 g) grated mozzarella cheese

1. Preheat air fryer at 180°C for 5 minutes.
2. For the tuna mix, place all ingredients in a small bowl and mix until well combined. Divide the mixture into 8 portions and shape into balls. Carefully roll each ball in panko to coat.
3. Lightly spray a shallow heatproof dish with oil (check it fits into your air fryer). Place balls in prepared dish. Cook in air fryer at 180°C for 6 minutes. Carefully turn balls, then cook at 180°C for a further 6 minutes or until golden.

- TO REFRIGERATE: Store bites in a reusable container for up to 3 days. Serve chilled or reheat in air fryer or microwave.

Wendy's tip

If you don't have an air fryer, place balls on a baking paper-lined tray. Lightly spray with oil and cook in a 180°C oven for 15 minutes or until lightly browned, turning halfway through.

See page 9 for details

Raspberry *banana bread*

2-3 **PersonalPoints range per serve** 

This is the one recipe my husband always requests whenever I'm in a baking mood. It's a favourite of his, so it never lasts very long when I make it! Perfect for morning or afternoon tea and a really great way to use up all your ripe bananas.

REBECCA

Serves 16 / *Prep* 15 minutes / *Cook* 45 minutes

1⅔ cups (250 g) self-raising flour
1 teaspoon baking powder
3 eggs, lightly beaten
4 ripe bananas, mashed
2 tablespoons (40 ml) skim milk
1 teaspoon ground cinnamon
½ cup (70 g) fresh or frozen raspberries
1 tablespoon (20 ml) maple syrup

1. Preheat oven to 160°C. Lightly spray a 12 cm x 24 cm loaf tin with oil and line base and sides with baking paper.
2. Place all ingredients in a large bowl and stir gently to combine.
3. Pour into prepared tin and bake for 45 minutes or until golden brown and cooked in the centre when tested with a skewer.
4. Stand in tin for 5 minutes, then turn out onto a wire rack to cool completely.
5. Cut into 16 slices.

- TO REFRIGERATE: Store bread in a reusable container for up to 1 week.
- TO FREEZE: Store individual slices in reusable snap-lock bags for up to 3 months. Thaw at room temperature.

See page 9 for details

Crumbed cheese wheels

3 PersonalPoints per cheese wheel 

My boys absolutely love cheese. Fried cheese? Who turns THAT down? These gooey cheese wheels with a crispy coating are full of flavour and perfect for dipping. Try sweet chilli sauce or your favourite chutney on the side.

WENDY

***Makes** 6 / **Prep** 5 minutes / **Cook** 15 minutes*

6 x 20 g light cheese wheels
1 egg
½ cup (30 g) panko breadcrumbs
2 teaspoons dried mixed herbs

1 Preheat oven to 200°C. Line a baking tray with baking paper (or a WW non-stick oven liner).

2 Remove cheese wheels from their packaging and wax casings.

3 Lightly beat egg in a small bowl. Place panko and herbs in a bowl. Dip cheese wheels in egg, then toss in panko mixture to coat evenly. Transfer to prepared baking tray. Lightly spray with oil and bake for 10–15 minutes, until golden. Serve immediately.

- TO REFRIGERATE: Crumb cheese wheels up to 2 days ahead and store, uncooked, in a single layer in a reusable container. Transfer to tray and bake following instructions in step 3.
- TO FREEZE: Store uncooked crumbed cheese wheels as above for up to 3 months. Transfer frozen wheels to tray and bake as above.

Wendy's tips

- You can also cook these in an air fryer at 180°C for about 10 minutes.
- I used light Babybel cheese wheels, but you can use any brand.

See page 9 for details

Smoked salmon & cream cheese mug muffin (page 197)

Pizza mug muffin (page 196)

Veggie mug muffin (page 196)

Taco-inspired mug muffin (page 197)

Rebecca's mighty mug muffins

Like most busy households, mornings at my place are hectic. The struggle to get myself and the kids out of bed, dressed, fed and out the door to make it to school and work on time is real. Mug muffins are super-speedy to make in the morning, or you can have them prepped and ready to eat on the run. Many mug muffin recipes are sweet, so I created a few recipes to satisfy my savoury tooth. I love experimenting with different flavour combinations. I've even made a gluten-free variety by replacing the oats with lupin flakes (available in health food stores). All microwaves are different, so experiment with the timings suggested in the recipes to ensure the best results from yours.

REBECCA

Pizza mug muffin

1-6 **PersonalPoints range per mug muffin**  

Pizza for breakfast? When it's this fast and this healthy, pizza is NEVER off the menu. My son always packs a couple of these into his bag to fill up on after rugby training.

Makes 1 / *Prep* 5 minutes / *Cook* 2 minutes

1 tablespoon (10 g) grated mozzarella cheese
⅓ cup (30 g) quick oats
1 egg
1 tablespoon (20 ml) skim milk
20 g 97% fat-free smoked ham, chopped
½ small tomato, cut into 1 cm pieces
1 green shallot (spring onion), white part only, thinly sliced

1 Reserve half the mozzarella. Place remaining mozzarella in a 350 ml capacity microwave-safe mug with remaining ingredients and mix until well combined. Top with reserved mozzarella.

2 Microwave on High (100%) for 1½–2 minutes, until muffin is just firm in the centre and starts to come away from the side of the mug. Serve warm.

- TO REFRIGERATE: Store my cooked mug muffins, covered in their mugs (without any toppings), for up to 3 days. Reheat in microwave and add toppings to serve.

- TO FREEZE: Store my cooked mug muffins as above for up to 2 months. Thaw overnight in fridge and serve cold or reheat in the microwave until hot, adding toppings to serve.

See page 9 for details

Veggie mug muffin

0-5 **PersonalPoints range per mug muffin**  

Whether you are trying to boost your veggie intake for the day, or looking to introduce a few vegetarian meals into your week, this mug muffin is a great place to start.

Makes 1 / *Prep* 5 minutes / *Cook* 2 minutes

⅓ cup (30 g) quick oats
1 egg
1 tablespoon (20 ml) skim milk
1 tablespoon finely chopped red onion
1 mushroom, finely chopped
2 teaspoons finely chopped fresh flat-leaf parsley
3 cherry tomatoes, halved

1 Place all ingredients in a 350 ml capacity microwave-safe mug. Season with salt and pepper and mix until well combined.

2 Microwave on High (100%) for 1½–2 minutes until muffin is just firm in the centre and starts to come away from the side of the mug. Serve warm.

See page 9 for details

Taco-inspired mug muffin

2-7 **PersonalPoints range per mug muffin** 

All the flavours of a Mexican taco in a perfectly portioned muffin. This recipe is my daughter's absolute favourite. She likes to enjoy it for lunch or afternoon tea instead of breakfast.

Makes *1* / ***Prep*** *5 minutes* / ***Cook*** *2 minutes*

⅓ cup (30 g) quick oats
1 egg
1 tablespoon (20 ml) light sour cream
2 teaspoons finely chopped red onion
2 teaspoons fresh or frozen corn kernels
2 teaspoons finely chopped red capsicum
1 tablespoon chopped fresh coriander
1 teaspoon taco seasoning

1. Place all ingredients in a 350 ml capacity microwave-safe mug. Season with salt and pepper and mix until well combined.
2. Microwave on High (100%) for 1½–2 minutes until muffin is just firm in the centre and starts to come away from the side of the mug. Serve warm.

See page 9 for details

Smoked salmon & cream cheese mug muffin

2-5 **PersonalPoints range per mug muffin**  

Out of all the mug muffin recipes I have made, this is hands-down my favourite combination of flavours. The lupin flakes give it a slightly earthy, nutty flavour, while the smoked salmon, cream cheese and avocado scream indulgence.

Makes *1* / ***Prep*** *10 minutes* / ***Cook*** *5 minutes*

20 g lupin flakes
1 large egg
1 tablespoon (20 ml) skim milk
30 g smoked salmon, chopped
1 x 16 g light cream cheese wedge, chopped
1 tablespoon chopped fresh dill
2 teaspoons chopped fresh chives
2 teaspoons mashed avocado

1. Place all ingredients, except avocado, in a 350 ml capacity microwave-safe mug. Season with salt and pepper and mix until well combined.
2. Microwave on High (100%) for 1½–2 minutes until muffin is just firm in the centre and starts to come away from the side of the mug. Serve warm, topped with avocado.

See page 9 for details

Dessert

60-second lemon *mug cake*

3-6 **PersonalPoints range per cake** 

In the mood for a quick dessert? Sixty seconds says it all. This light and fluffy cake topped with a sweet and zesty topping ticks all the boxes.

WENDY

Makes 1 / *Prep* 10 minutes / *Cook* 1 minute

2 tablespoons (25 g) self-raising flour
½ teaspoon baking powder
1 teaspoon monk fruit sweetener
1 egg
1 teaspoon finely grated lemon zest, plus extra to serve
1 teaspoon lemon juice

TOPPING
2 tablespoons (40 g) 99% fat-free plain yoghurt
1 tablespoon (20 ml) sugar-free maple syrup
½ teaspoon icing sugar
1 teaspoon lemon juice

1 Lightly spray a 1 cup (250 ml) capacity microwave-safe mug with oil. Place flour, baking powder and sweetener in a small bowl. Add egg, lemon zest and juice and whisk with a fork until well combined. Spoon mixture into prepared mug. Microwave on High (100%) for 1 minute or until set in the centre.

2 Meanwhile, to make topping, combine all ingredients in a small bowl. Pour topping over hot mug muffin and sprinkle with extra lemon zest to serve.

- TO REFRIGERATE: Store cooked cake, covered, in mug, without topping, for up to 2 days. Reheat in microwave. Store topping separately in a reusable container for up to 3 days, or make when ready to serve.
- TO FREEZE: Store cooked cake in mug, without topping, for up to 2 months. Thaw overnight in fridge and serve cold or reheat in the microwave until hot. Finish with topping when ready to serve.

Wendy's tip

Depending on the wattage of your microwave, you may need to microwave the mug muffin for an extra 30 seconds.

See page 9 for details

Jaffa *jelly* slice

1-5 **PersonalPoints range per serve** 

When I was young, I only had jelly slice at birthday parties as a treat. This version is much higher in protein and soluble fibre, and has a very low saturated-fat content, meaning jelly slice can now be a regular treat! REBECCA

Serves *8* / ***Prep*** *25 minutes + chilling*

BASE

1 cup (90 g) quick oats
200 g medjool dates, pitted and quartered
1 tablespoon (10 g) cocoa powder
1 tablespoon finely grated orange zest

FILLING

9 g sachet low-sugar orange and mango jelly crystals
400 g 99% fat-free plain Greek yoghurt

TOPPING

9 g sachet low-sugar orange and mango jelly crystals
5 g no-added-sugar dark chocolate

1. Lightly spray a 16 cm x 26 cm slice tin with oil and line base and sides with baking paper, extending paper 3 cm above edge of tin.
2. To make base, process all ingredients and 2 tablespoons water in a food processor until mixture comes together in a ball. Using damp fingertips, press mixture over base of prepared tin.
3. To make filling, mix jelly crystals with 2 tablespoons boiling water in a small jug until dissolved. Process jelly mixture and yoghurt in clean food processor until combined. Pour mixture over base. Refrigerate for 2–3 hours, until set.
4. Meanwhile, to make topping, mix jelly crystals with ½ cup (125 ml) boiling water in a jug until dissolved, then stir in ½ cup (125 ml) cold water. Stand at room temperature for 1 hour, stirring occasionally. Transfer to the fridge for the last hour of the filling setting time or until it starts to thicken, but don't allow it to set.
5. Pour topping over the back of a dessertspoon over filling (pouring over a spoon prevents damaging the top of the slice). Refrigerate for 2–3 hours, until topping is set.
6. To serve, use the lining paper to carefully lift the slice from tin. Grate chocolate over the top. Cut into 8 pieces.

- **TO REFRIGERATE:** Store slice in a single layer in a reusable container for up to 5 days.

Rebecca's tip

For a firm, crunchy base, bake at 180°C for 20 minutes and cool completely before topping with the filling.

See page 9 for details

Peanut butter muffins

 **PersonalPoints range per muffin** 

Peanut butter is one of my lifelong loves and these muffins are a peanut butter lover's healthy dream. Enjoy them for breakfast or as a tea time indulgence, or pop them into your lunch box.

WENDY

Makes 6 / *Prep* 10 minutes / *Cook* 30 minutes

100 g rolled oats
50 g almond meal
35 g unsalted cashews, finely chopped
40 g monk fruit sweetener
2 teaspoons baking powder
2 eggs, lightly beaten
½ cup (125 g) mashed banana

PEANUT BUTTER TOPPING
20 g natural peanut butter (100% nuts)
1 tablespoon (20 ml) sugar-free maple syrup

1 Preheat oven to 180°C. Lightly spray 6 x 105 ml silicone muffin moulds with oil (or use the WW silicone muffin moulds) and place on a baking tray.

2 Mix oats, almond meal, cashews, sweetener and baking powder in a medium bowl. Add eggs and banana. Stir until well combined. Spoon mixture evenly into muffin moulds. Bake for 25–30 minutes or until just firm in the centre when lightly touched with fingertips. Cool muffins in moulds, then remove and transfer to a wire rack.

3 Meanwhile, to make topping, microwave peanut butter in a small microwave-safe bowl on High (100%) for 30 seconds. Stir in syrup until smooth and combined. Spread evenly over muffins.

- **TO REFRIGERATE:** Store peanut butter-topped muffins for up to 3 days or plain muffins (without topping) for up to 1 week in a reusable container.

- **TO FREEZE:** Store plain muffins (without topping) in a reusable container for up to 3 months. Thaw at room temperature. Spread with topping just before serving.

See page 9 for details

Strawberry flummery

1-2 **PersonalPoints range per serve**  

Flummery is a soft mousse-like dessert made with just a few basic ingredients. This old-school recipe is my mum's and it always takes me back to my childhood. I love to tuck into this after dinner.

WENDY

Serves *6* / ***Prep*** *15 minutes + chilling*

9 g sachet low-sugar strawberry jelly crystals
250 g fresh strawberries, sliced
1 cup (250 ml) light evaporated milk, well chilled

1. Place jelly crystals in a small heatproof bowl. Add 50 ml boiling water and stir until crystals are dissolved. Reserve 200 g strawberries in fridge.

2. Process remaining strawberries and jelly mixture in a food processor until smooth. Set aside.

3. Beat evaporated milk in a large bowl with electric beaters until thick and doubled in volume. Add strawberry mixture and whisk to combine. Pour into a deep 20 cm round serving bowl. Refrigerate for 1 hour or until set. Scatter over reserved sliced strawberries to serve.

- **TO REFRIGERATE:** Store flummery, covered, for up to 3 days. Top with reserved strawberries just before serving.

Wendy's tip

For maximum volume when beating, make sure you chill the evaporated milk in the fridge overnight, before making the flummery.

See page 9 for details

Citrus *jelly* cheesecake

1-3 **PersonalPoints range per serve** 

I LOVE cheesecake. However the PersonalPoints of a traditional slice are through the roof! My version is so low in PersonalPoints and high in protein, it's a treat you can enjoy regularly. I like to use citrus jelly, but you can use any flavour that takes your fancy.

REBECCA

Serves 8 / *Prep* 25 minutes + chilling / *Cook* 1 minute

BASE

6 medjool dates, pitted and chopped
½ cup (45 g) rolled oats
1 tablespoon (5 g) desiccated coconut

LEMON CHEESECAKE FILLING

9 g sachet low-sugar lemon jelly crystals
300 g 97% fat-free cottage cheese

LIME TOPPING

9 g sachet low-sugar lime jelly crystals
2 teaspoons shredded coconut

Rebecca's tip

For a firmer base, bake at 180°C for 20 minutes and cool completely before filling.

1 Remove side from a 20 cm springform tin. Place a sheet of baking paper over base, then secure side over base to hold the paper lining in place.

2 To make base, combine dates and 1 tablespoon water in a microwave-safe bowl and microwave on High (100%) for 1 minute. Transfer dates to a food processor with rolled oats and desiccated coconut and process until well combined. Using damp fingertips, press mixture over base of prepared tin. Set aside in fridge while preparing filling.

3 To make filling, mix lemon jelly crystals with 2 tablespoons boiling water in a small jug until dissolved. Process jelly mixture, cottage cheese and 1 cup (250 ml) cold water in clean food processor until combined. Pour mixture over the base. Refrigerate for 2–3 hours, until set.

4 Meanwhile, to make topping, mix lime jelly crystals with ½ cup (125 ml) boiling water in a jug until dissolved, then stir in ½ cup (125 ml) cold water. Stand at room temperature for 1 hour, stirring occasionally. Transfer to the fridge for the last hour of the filling setting time or until it starts to thicken, but don't allow it to set.

5 Pour liquid jelly over the back of a dessertspoon over filling. Refrigerate for 2–3 hours, until jelly is set.

6 To serve, carefully remove the outer ring of the springform tin. Sprinkle top with shredded coconut. Cut into 8 wedges.

- **TO REFRIGERATE:** Store cheesecake in a reusable container for up to 5 days.

See page 9 for details

No-bake chocolate slice

2-3 **PersonalPoints range per serve** 

It is time to fill up your baking tin with my delicious chocolate slice. This recipe is a huge hit with kids who can't say no to anything chocolatey. It's also great for using up all the crumbly bits at the bottom of your cereal box.

WENDY

Serves *12* / ***Prep*** *20 minutes + chilling* / ***Cook*** *1 minute*

10 medjool dates, pitted
5 x 15 g cereal wheat biscuits, broken
2 tablespoons (15 g) cocoa powder
1 teaspoon vanilla extract
1 tablespoon (20 ml) sugar-free maple syrup
120 g WW hazelnut cocoa spread

1. Lightly spray an 18 cm x 28 cm slice tin or shallow dish with oil and line base and sides with baking paper.

2. Combine dates and ¼ cup (60 ml) boiling water in a microwave-safe bowl. Microwave on High (100%) for 1 minute. Drain.

3. Transfer dates to a food processor. Add cereal wheat biscuits, cocoa, vanilla and syrup and process until well combined. If needed, add 1 tablespoon boiling water and pulse to bring ingredients together. Press mixture evenly into prepared dish and spread with hazelnut cocoa spread. Cover and refrigerate for about 2 hours or until firm. Lift slice from dish with lining paper. Cut into 12 pieces.

- **TO REFRIGERATE:** Store slice in a reusable container for up to 1 week.
- **TO FREEZE:** Store slice as above for up to 3 months. Enjoy straight from the freezer, or allow to thaw in the fridge before serving.

Wendy's tip

I used Weet-Bix but you can use any brand of cereal wheat biscuits.

See page 9 for details

Coffee, oat & date loaf

Afternoon tea? Don't mind if I do. This coffee-flavoured loaf would have to be the most requested sweet recipe I have created, and when it's this low in PersonalPoints, why wouldn't you indulge?

REBECCA

Serves *8* / ***Prep*** *15 minutes* / ***Cook*** *40 minutes*

2 teaspoons instant coffee powder
200 g (about 13) medjool dates, pitted and finely chopped
2 teaspoons bicarbonate of soda
2 cups (180 g) quick oats

1 Preheat oven to 160°C.

2 Dissolve coffee in 1 cup (250 ml) boiling water in a heatproof jug. Pour over dates in a medium microwave-safe bowl. Microwave on High (100%) for 1 minute. Stir in bicarbonate of soda and mash dates to break them down and combine well (mixture will fizz up a bit).

3 Add oats to date mixture and mix well. If mixture looks dry, stir in some more hot water, it should be the consistency of thick porridge.

4 Spoon mixture into a lightly oiled and baking paper-lined 12 cm x 22 cm loaf tin (or a WW silicone loaf tin). Bake for 30–40 minutes or until a skewer inserted in the centre comes out clean. Cool in tin, then turn out and cut into 8 slices. Enjoy as is or toast slices to serve, if preferred.

- **TO REFRIGERATE:** Store loaf in a reusable container for up to 5 days.
- **TO FREEZE:** Wrap slices individually and store in a reusable container or freezer bag for up to 3 months. Thaw at room temperature.

Rebecca's tip

For a more intense coffee flavour, use an espresso shot and add enough boiling water to make up 1 cup (250 ml) liquid. For a different flavour, replace coffee with vanilla bean paste, cocoa or drinking chocolate.

See page 9 for details

Nannie's *lemon* cheesecake

9-10 **PersonalPoints range per serve** 

Cheesecakes can be made in advance, meaning there's one less thing to do on a busy day. This recipe, dedicated to my dear friend and WW member Danielle, features a gingery biscuit base topped with a zesty lemon cheesecake topping. Dig in!

WENDY

Serves 9 / Prep 20 minutes + chilling

BISCUIT BASE

20 x 17 g milk chocolate digestive biscuits
2 teaspoons ground ginger
1 tablespoon (20 g) reduced-fat oil spread, melted
2 tablespoons (40 ml) sugar-free maple syrup

CHEESECAKE TOPPING

9 g sachet low-sugar lemon jelly crystals
2 eggs, separated
2 tablespoons (40 ml) lemon juice
2 tablespoons (30 g) monk fruit sweetener
1 cup (250 g) 97% fat-free cottage cheese
Dried lemon slices or finely grated lemon zest, to decorate (see tip)

Wendy's tip

If you have a dehydrator at home, dry some lemon slices and use as a topping for the cheesecake – they complement it beautifully.

1 To start on topping, place jelly crystals in a small heatproof bowl. Add 1 cup (250 ml) boiling water and stir until crystals are dissolved. Stand at room temperature until cool but not set.

2 Meanwhile, to make base, lightly spray a 1.5 litre (6 cup) capacity serving dish with oil. Process biscuits in a food processor until finely crushed. Add ginger, oil spread and syrup. Pulse to combine. Press mixture over base of prepared dish. Refrigerate while making topping.

3 To finish topping, beat egg yolks, lemon juice, sweetener and cottage cheese in a bowl with electric beaters until smooth and thick. Whisk in cooled jelly mixture until combined. Set aside. Beat egg whites in a separate medium bowl with clean electric beaters until stiff peaks form, then fold through cottage cheese mixture.

4 Pour topping over biscuit base. Refrigerate for 3 hours or until set. Decorate top with dried lemon slices or lemon zest. Spoon into bowls to serve.

- **TO REFRIGERATE:** Store cheesecake, covered in serving dish, for up to 5 days.

See page 9 for details

Lemon-glazed *tea cakes*

6–7 PersonalPoints range per cake

Two favourite childhood memories I have of my mum are endless cups of tea and lemon-glazed cakes in our lunch boxes. I created this recipe as a nod to both. Each year on Mother's Day, I whip up a batch and enjoy them with Mum.

REBECCA

Makes 12 / *Prep* 25 minutes / *Cook* 25 minutes

2 tablespoons (5 g) Earl Grey tea leaves
½ cup (110 g) sugar
¼ cup (60 g) reduced-fat oil spread
1 teaspoon vanilla bean paste
3 eggs
1½ cups (225 g) self-raising flour
½ cup (120 g) 99% fat-free plain Greek yoghurt

LEMON GLAZE

2 tablespoons (20 g) icing sugar
2 teaspoons finely shredded lemon zest

1 Preheat oven to 170°C. Lightly spray 12 mini loaf tins (6 cm x 11 cm) with oil and line bases with baking paper.

2 Process tea leaves and sugar in a small food processor until finely ground.

3 Beat oil spread, tea mixture and vanilla in a bowl with electric beaters until creamy. Beat in eggs, 1 at a time, until combined. Gradually beat in half the flour on low speed, then beat in half the yoghurt. Repeat with remaining flour and yoghurt until just combined (don't overmix).

4 Pour mixture evenly into lined tins. Bake for 20–25 minutes or until a skewer inserted in the centre of cakes comes out clean. Stand cakes in tins for 10 minutes before turning out onto a wire rack to cool completely.

5 To make glaze, mix icing sugar, half the lemon zest and 2 teaspoons water in a small bowl until smooth. Drizzle glaze over each cake and sprinkle with the remaining lemon zest. Stand until set before serving.

- **TO REFRIGERATE:** Store cakes in a single layer in a reusable container for up to 5 days.
- **TO FREEZE:** Store cakes as above for up to 3 months. Thaw at room temperature.

See page 9 for details

No-fuss apple turnover

3-9 PersonalPoints range per turnover 

That's right, this apple turnover is fuss-free. Made with the WW omelette maker, it really is the ultimate kitchen hack. Enjoy it as a tasty treat for breakfast or dessert.

WENDY

Makes 1 / Prep 5 minutes / Cook 1½ minutes

2 tablespoons (25 g) self-raising flour
1 teaspoon monk fruit sweetener
½ teaspoon ground cinnamon
1 egg
200 g canned pie apple (100% apple)

1 Whisk flour, sweetener, cinnamon, egg and half the apple in a small bowl until combined. Spoon mixture into a WW omelette maker. Microwave on High (100%) for 1½ minutes.

2 Carefully turn out onto a plate, fill with the remaining apple and fold over to serve.

- **TO REFRIGERATE:** Store turnover, covered, without filling (with remaining apple mixture in a separate container) for up to 1 day. Add remaining apples, following step 2 just before serving. Enjoy it chilled or microwave until warm.

Wendy's tip

This is delicious served with a little sugar-free maple syrup, 99% fat-free plain yoghurt, reduced-fat ice cream or a dusting of icing sugar or cinnamon.

See page 9 for details

Raspberry lattice tart

6 PersonalPoints per serve  

When you are looking for a dessert to wow your loved ones, look no further than my raspberry lattice tart. The stunning ruby-red raspberry filling glinting through the crunchy browned pastry is sure to impress.

REBECCA

Serves 8 / Prep 25 minutes / Cook 50 minutes

40 g caster sugar
300 g frozen raspberries
1 tablespoon (10 g) cornflour
1½ sheets (270 g) frozen reduced-fat shortcrust pastry, just thawed

1 To make raspberry filling, place sugar and 200 g raspberries in a saucepan over medium heat and bring to a simmer. Simmer, stirring occasionally, for 5 minutes or until reduced by one-third. Whisk in cornflour and simmer, stirring, for a further 2 minutes or until mixture thickens slightly. Remove from heat, cool for 10 minutes, then fold through remaining raspberries. Set aside to cool completely.

2 Preheat oven to 180°C and line base of an 18 cm loose-base fluted round tart tin with baking paper. Gently press the whole pastry sheet over base and up side of tin. Cut halved pastry sheet lengthways into 16 long, thin strips.

3 Pour raspberry mixture into pastry case, then arrange pastry strips over filling in a criss-cross pattern and press around edge to seal. Trim off overhanging pastry. Bake for 35–40 minutes, until golden. Remove from oven and cool in tin for 10 minutes before serving.

- **TO REFRIGERATE:** Store tart in a reusable container in the fridge for up to 5 days. Enjoy cold or reheat in microwave until warmed through.
- **TO FREEZE:** Wrap individual slices and store in a reusable container for up to 3 months. Thaw slices at room temperature and serve cold, or warm in microwave.

Rebecca's tip

If you can't find reduced-fat pastry, just use regular shortcrust pastry for 1 extra PersonalPoint.

See page 9 for details

Carrot cake *sandwiches* with cream cheese icing

3-6 **PersonalPoints range per cake** 

This has to be my favourite sweet treat of all time! I came up with the recipe one night as I hunted through the entire kitchen for cake. I didn't find anything that came close, so I decided to whip up my own instead. Made using the WW omelette maker poacher insert, this cake is ready in just 20 minutes.

REBECCA

Makes 2 / Prep 15 minutes / Cook 2 minutes

- 1 egg, lightly beaten
- 1 small carrot, unpeeled, grated
- 2 medjool dates, pitted and finely chopped
- ½ teaspoon ground cinnamon
- ½ teaspoon mixed spice
- ½ teaspoon ground ginger
- 2 tablespoons (25 g) self-raising flour
- 1 x 16 g light cream cheese wedge
- 2 teaspoons icing sugar

1. Mix egg, carrot, dates and spices in a small bowl, then stir in flour until combined.
2. Spread half the mixture into the WW 2-in-1 egg poacher and omelette maker. Close omelette maker and microwave on High (100%) for 1 minute. Turn cakes out onto a wire rack to cool. Repeat with the remaining mixture.
3. Mix cheese and icing sugar in a small bowl until smooth. Spread icing over cake tops, then sandwich cakes together to make 2 layered cakes.

- **TO REFRIGERATE:** Store uniced cakes for up to 5 days, or iced cakes for up to 3 days, in a reusable container.
- **TO FREEZE:** Store uniced cakes as above for up to 2 months. Thaw at room temperature and ice just before serving.

Rebecca's tip

Try this as mug muffins. After step 1, divide between 2 x 350 ml capacity microwave-safe mugs. Cook on High (100%) for 2 minutes, or until a skewer inserted in the centre comes out clean. Spread icing over muffin tops.

See page 9 for details

Salted 'toffee' fudge balls

1-2 PersonalPoints range per ball

This recipe turns the humble date into a sweet and salty caramel treat. The secret is eating them straight from the freezer to keep the chewy, toffee texture.

WENDY

Makes 24 / *Prep* 20 minutes + chilling / *Cook* 1 minute

440 g medjool dates, pitted and finely chopped
2 tablespoons (45 g) natural peanut butter (100% nuts)
1 teaspoon vanilla essence
55 g almond meal

1 Place dates in a microwave-safe bowl and pour over 2 tablespoons boiling water. Microwave on High (100%) for 45 seconds.

2 Transfer dates to a food processor, add remaining ingredients and process until a smooth, thick paste forms. Cover and refrigerate for 30 minutes, or until chilled.

3 Roll tablespoons of mixture into 24 balls and place in a large reusable container lined with baking paper. Cover with lid and place in the freezer for 2 hours or until firm to the touch. Sprinkle with sea salt flakes just before serving.

- TO FREEZE: Follow instructions in step 3 and keep for up to 3 months.

Wendy's tips

- The secret to perfectly portioned balls is to weigh the total mixture, then divide by the number of balls you want to make.
- You can use almond butter instead of peanut butter, if you prefer.

See page 9 for details

Mango & passionfruit mug muffin

 **PersonalPoints range per mug muffin** 

A lot of mug muffins use mashed banana as the base, but I'm not a big fan. On a quest to come up with a banana-free mug muffin, I developed this winning tropical combo of mango and passionfruit. Ready in under 10 minutes, it's delicious for breakfast, as a snack or for dessert.

REBECCA

Makes 1 / Prep 5 minutes / Cook 2 minutes

½ mango, chopped
1 passionfruit, halved
1 egg
⅓ cup (30 g) quick oats
1 tablespoon (20 g) 99% fat-free plain yoghurt

1 Mash the mango with half the passionfruit pulp in a small bowl. Whisk in egg, then stir in oats until combined. Spoon into a 1 cup (250 ml) capacity microwave-safe mug.

2 Microwave on High (100%) for 1½–2 minutes until muffin is just firm in the centre. Serve warm, topped with yoghurt and remaining passionfruit.

- **TO REFRIGERATE:** Store cooked muffin, covered, in the mug (without any toppings) for up to 3 days. Reheat in microwave and add toppings to serve.
- **TO FREEZE:** Store as above for up to 2 months. Thaw overnight in fridge and enjoy cold or microwave until warm. Add toppings just before serving.

See page 9 for details

Rocky road *bliss* balls

1–2 PersonalPoints range per ball 

Bliss balls are one of the best snacks to have on hand. These are my favourite to make, especially around Christmas time, as they boast marshmallows, cherries and everything else you'd expect to find in a delicious rocky road treat.

WENDY

Makes *12* / ***Prep*** *30 minutes + chilling*

- 10 g unsalted pistachios, coarsely chopped
- 100 g rolled oats
- 1 teaspoon cocoa powder
- 4 medjool dates, pitted and finely chopped
- 2 glacé cherries, finely chopped
- 3 teaspoons sugar-free maple syrup
- 20 g pink and white marshmallows, finely chopped
- 10 g dark chocolate chips
- ½ teaspoon almond essence

1 Place all ingredients in a large bowl. Mix well until ingredients are combined and mixture starts to clump together, adding 1–2 tablespoons warm water if needed.

2 Shape tablespoons of mixture into 12 balls. Place balls in a single layer in a reusable container. Refrigerate for 1 hour or until firm, before serving.

- **TO REFRIGERATE:** Store bliss balls in a reusable container for up to 2 weeks.

Wendy's tip

I love almond essence in these bliss balls, but you could also try peppermint or vanilla essence.

See page 9 for details

Easy apple & gingerbread cake

There is something very special about the smell of freshly baked gingerbread cake. Warming ginger, nutmeg and cinnamon, mixed with the sweetness of apple, is a match made in heaven. Simply process all ingredients together in just one step, then enjoy it straight from the oven or cold in a snack box.

REBECCA

Serves *24 /* ***Prep*** *10 minutes /* ***Cook*** *40 minutes*

400 g can pie apple (100% apple)
2 large eggs
1 teaspoon ground ginger
1 teaspoon ground cinnamon
1 teaspoon ground nutmeg
1 teaspoon ground allspice
¼ teaspoon ground cloves
1 cup (160 g) wholemeal self-raising flour
2 teaspoons baking powder
¼ cup (55 g) raw sugar

1. Preheat oven to 170°C. Lightly spray a 21 cm square cake tin with oil and line base and sides with baking paper.

2. Process all ingredients in a food processor until combined. Pour mixture into prepared tin. Bake for 40 minutes or until golden and a skewer inserted in the centre comes out clean.

3. Stand in tin for 5 minutes, then turn out onto a wire rack to cool. Cut into 24 squares.

- **TO REFRIGERATE:** Store cake in a reusable container for up to 5 days.
- **TO FREEZE:** Wrap slices individually and store in a reusable container or freezer bag for up to 3 months. Thaw at room temperature.

See page 9 for details

Cheat's mini chocolate 'donuts'

Craving donuts? Grab a packet of brioche slider buns for a clever and quick hack. Here I use a decadent chocolate filling, but you can get creative with different filling options. They're best served fresh, so avoid storing any extra. You can easily split the recipe in four if you only want to make one.

WENDY

Makes 4 / Prep 10 minutes / Cook 5 minutes

4 x 20 g mini brioche slider buns
1 teaspoon reduced-fat oil spread, melted
2 tablespoons (30 g) monk fruit sweetener

FILLING
20 g sachet 99% sugar-free drinking chocolate
100 g 99% fat-free plain yoghurt

1. Heat brioche buns in an air fryer at 180°C for 4–5 minutes, until warm.
2. Meanwhile, to make filling, combine drinking chocolate and yoghurt in a small bowl. Transfer to a small reusable piping bag, fitted with a 1 cm plain nozzle.
3. Using a pastry brush, lightly brush buns with oil spread, then roll in sweetener to coat. Gently make a hole in the middle of each bun and pipe in filling. Serve.

Wendy's tips

- It's not essential to heat the brioche buns. Use them straight from the packet, if you prefer.
- Reusable piping bags are available from major supermarkets and kitchenware stores.

See page 9 for details

Acknowledgements

A book like this comes together through the incredibly hard work of an amazing team, and I am so very honoured to have had the privilege to work alongside some truly inspirational people. At my first WW workshop over 20 years ago, never did I imagine that I would become a Coach, let alone be asked to create recipes for a cookbook like the very ones I used to lose weight!

Firstly, thank you to the Pan Macmillan team: Ingrid Ohlsson, Lucinda Thompson, Ariane Durkin, Madeleine Kane, Naomi van Groll and Candice Wyman. Without your vision, this book would not be here! Thank you for your belief in me and the trust you put in me to bring my recipes to life.

My sincerest gratitude goes to my WW team, without whom none of this would have been possible. Trusha Madhoo, Katherine Christie, Jade Leung and Chrisy Christou – thank you for all the support, advice, editing, guidance and especially the hand-holding along the way! I am so very proud of what we have created together, and eternally grateful for the confidence you have all given me to believe in myself. The process of putting this book together was made so easy by the absolute professionalism and dedication you all possess. A special thank you also to Kathy Golding and Miche Bloch. Thank you both for the complete faith you have always had in me. I am blessed to have you in my life.

To my ever-patient and loving husband, Michael. I can't think of anyone else I would want to do life with! You have always been my chief supporter, leader of my cheer squad and my shoulder to cry on. Thank you for loving me unconditionally. I'm sure my 'So, I've been thinking . . .' statements fill you with apprehension; however you always go along with my out-there ideas and our life is richer for the experiences. As I said on our wedding day: To the world you are my husband, but to me you are my world.

Andy and Emily, you are my heartbeat. I am so proud to be your mum. You both inspire me in more ways than I can count. You were my motivation for ensuring I reached my weight-loss goal, my reason to be healthy every day. Thank you both for helping me create new recipes, for always being willing to try anything I cook, and for all your honest feedback after every taste-testing session. And yes, you can both lick the bowl after the next cake is made!

My passion for food and family comes from my beautiful mum, nana and granny. You taught me how to cook, how to love and how to be a strong, independent woman. Thank you for sharing your enthusiasm, your knowledge and your appreciation for good food and great recipes.

And finally, thank you to you, the reader! I hope I have inspired you to cook from your heart and to have the belief in yourself that you can reach your goals.

My dream to bring out a beautiful cookbook and to share my love of cooking and baking with anyone and everyone who loved food would never have come to reality without the amazing WW team who believed in me. I am so proud of our cookbook and terribly humbled. I'm still pinching myself and will probably do so each time I open this cookbook for years to come!

My gratitude to the incredible team at Pan Macmillan, especially to Ingrid Ohlsson, Lucinda Thompson, Ariane Durkin, Madeleine Kane, Naomi van Groll and Candice Wyman. Thank you for the opportunity to have my recipes published. It's a dream come true.

To the absolutely amazing WW team that I have worked so closely with over the last few months: a HUGE thank you to everyone that was involved in this project. Trusha Madhoo, thank you for this amazing opportunity and for making my dream come true. Thank you from the bottom of my heart for believing in me, my work and my passion for cooking and creating. Katherine Christie, thank you for being there every step of the way. Your guidance and support has been so invaluable in the creation of this cookbook. To my area manager Karla Forsyth, thank you for always supporting me and believing in me more than I believe in myself. I am grateful for all the guidance and support you have given me as a WW Coach over the past three years, both professionally and personally.

To all the lovely friendships I have made on my WW journey, thank you to each and every one of you. Special mention to my wonderful friend Michelle Celander, for your ongoing friendship and guidance. You mean the world to me. Anna Van Dyken, for your continuous guidance and friendship, thank you. Jonathan Fitzgerald, for always being a message away. So blessed with a WW family!

To my friends and family who taste-tested my recipes over and over again, especially Danielle. Thank you for being such a wonderful, trustworthy friend. You have a very special place in my heart.

Last but definitely not least, everything I do is for my sons. They are my WHY and will always be. Korban Heath and Luka – this is for you! Never stop believing in your dreams! May this always be a reminder that you can achieve anything in life if you work hard and believe in yourself. Mommy loves you both with all her heart.

To my mother, my absolute best friend in life, this is for YOU too! You have always believed in me and supported me. Thank you! I love you with all my heart.

I hope that everyone will find a very special recipe in this book that will become a favourite in your home too.

Wendy

Conversion chart

Measuring cups and spoons may vary slightly from one country to another, but the difference is generally not enough to affect a recipe. All cup and spoon measures are level. One Australian metric measuring cup holds 250 ml (8 fl oz), one Australian tablespoon holds 20 ml (4 teaspoons) and one Australian metric teaspoon holds 5 ml. North America, New Zealand and the UK use a 15 ml (3-teaspoon) tablespoon.

LENGTH

METRIC	IMPERIAL
3 mm	⅛ inch
6 mm	¼ inch
1 cm	½ inch
2.5 cm	1 inch
5 cm	2 inches
18 cm	7 inches
20 cm	8 inches
23 cm	9 inches
25 cm	10 inches
30 cm	12 inches

LIQUID MEASURES

ONE AMERICAN PINT	ONE IMPERIAL PINT
500 ml (16 fl oz)	600 ml (20 fl oz)

CUP	METRIC	IMPERIAL
⅛ cup	30 ml	1 fl oz
¼ cup	60 ml	2 fl oz
⅓ cup	80 ml	2½ fl oz
½ cup	125 ml	4 fl oz
⅔ cup	160 ml	5 fl oz
¾ cup	180 ml	6 fl oz
1 cup	250 ml	8 fl oz
2 cups	500 ml	16 fl oz
2¼ cups	560 ml	20 fl oz
4 cups	1 litre	32 fl oz

OVEN TEMPERATURES

CELSIUS	FAHRENHEIT
100°C	200°F
120°C	250°F
150°C	300°F
160°C	325°F
180°C	350°F
200°C	400°F
220°C	425°F

CELSIUS	GAS MARK
110°C	¼
130°C	½
140°C	1
150°C	2
170°C	3
180°C	4
190°C	5
200°C	6
220°C	7
230°C	8
240°C	9
250°C	10

DRY MEASURES

The most accurate way to measure dry ingredients is to weigh them. However, if using a cup, add the ingredient loosely to the cup and level with a knife; don't compact the ingredient unless the recipe states 'firmly packed'.

METRIC	IMPERIAL
15 g	½ oz
30 g	1 oz
60 g	2 oz
125 g	4 oz (¼ lb)
185 g	6 oz
250 g	8 oz (½ lb)
375 g	12 oz (¾ lb)
500 g	16 oz (1 lb)
1 kg	32 oz (2 lb)

Index

3-ingredient beer bread 170
60-second lemon mug cake 200

A

Air-fryer tuna melt bites 188
Apple & cinnamon pancakes 56
Apple pie scrolls 179
apples
- Apple & cinnamon pancakes 56
- Easy apple & gingerbread cake 226
- Apple pie scrolls 179
- No-fuss apple turnover 216
- Overnight bircher 60

asparagus
- Brown rice tuna sushi rolls 100

Avo pancakes 57
Avocado boat prawn cocktails 83
avocados
- Avo pancakes 57
- Avocado boat prawn cocktails 83
- Beef taco cups 86
- Chicken & avo pasta salad 80
- Creamy avo sauce 80
- Smoked salmon & cream cheese mug muffin 197
- Wasabi miso fish bowl 90

B

bacon
- Bacon & veggie slice 98
- Cheese & bacon breakfast muffins 58
- Chicken & bacon quiches with chickpea crust 82
- Freezable egg & bacon muffins 62
- Hash brown stacks with bacon & eggs 70

Bacon & veggie slice 98
baked beans, Stove-top 54
bananas
- Berry flake breakfast bars 55
- High-fibre banana loaves 174
- Nutty date & banana crispbreads 169
- Peanut butter muffins 204
- Raspberry banana bread 190
- Salted caramel protein overnight oats 66
- Strawberry cereal breakfast muffins 52

Bang bang chicken salad 76
beans
- Beef taco cups 86
- Quinoa & black bean patties 144
- Stove-top baked beans 54

beef
- Beef & feta patties 145
- Beef taco cups 86
- Dad's slow-braised beef (trinchado) 130
- Mince curry & egg pie (Babotie) 129
- Slow-cooked beef cheek lasagne 136
- Slow-cooker osso buco 111
- Tuscan beef & lentil stew 126

Beef & feta patties 145
Beef taco cups 86
berries
- Coconut chia overnight oats 50
- Overnight bircher 60
- Raspberry banana bread 190
- Raspberry lattice tart 218
- Strawberry cereal breakfast muffins 52
- Strawberry flummery 206
- Strawberry tray bake pancakes 72

Berry flake breakfast bars 55
bircher, Overnight 60
bliss balls, Rocky road 225
bliss bites, Choc-nut energy 172
Blue cheese-stuffed dates 187
bolognese, Lamb 148
'Bottom of the fridge' pasta bake 112
bread
- 3-ingredient beer bread 170
- Easy garlic naan 124
- Raspberry banana bread 190
- Sweet orange bread 164
- *see also* crispbread, loaves

broccoli
- Cauli rice nasi goreng with prawns 114
- Slow-cooker garlic honey chicken 104

Brown rice tuna sushi rolls 100
butter, Garlic not- 123

C

cakes
- 60-second lemon mug cake 200
- Carrot cake sandwiches with cream cheese icing 220
- Citrus jelly cheesecake 208
- Easy apple & gingerbread cake 226
- Lemon-glazed tea cakes 214
- Nannie's lemon cheesecake 212

capsicum
- 'Bottom of the fridge' pasta bake 112
- Chicken & avo pasta salad 80
- Chicken goulash with pasta 138
- Chicken stir-fry with chilli, basil and cashews 152
- Mum's curried pasta salad 88
- Spanish rice 158
- Taco-inspired mug muffin 197

Carrot cake sandwiches with cream cheese icing 220
carrots
- Bacon & veggie slice 98
- Beef taco cups 86
- 'Bottom of the fridge' pasta bake 112
- Brown rice tuna sushi rolls 100
- Carrot cake sandwiches with cream cheese icing 220
- Cauli rice nasi goreng with prawns 114
- Chicken & bacon quiches with chickpea crust 82
- Chicken sausage rolls 78
- Chicken stir-fry with chilli, basil and cashews 152
- Curried chicken drumsticks with rice 134
- Greek lamb meatballs with zoodles 132
- Lamb bolognese 148
- Pork fried rice 140
- Slow-cooker garlic honey chicken 104
- tomato sauce 132
- Tuscan beef & lentil stew 126
- Wasabi miso fish bowl 90

Cauli rice nasi goreng with prawns 114
cauliflower
- Cauli rice nasi goreng with prawns 114
- Slow-cooker red lentil & sweet potato curry 154

celery
- Chicken goulash with pasta 138
- Slow-cooker osso buco 111
- Tuscan beef & lentil stew 126

Cheat's mini chocolate 'donuts' 228
Cheat's seafood marinara pizza 116

cheese
Air-fryer tuna melt bites 188
Bacon & veggie slice 98
Beef & feta patties 145
Blue cheese-stuffed dates 187
'Bottom of the fridge' pasta bake 112
Carrot cake sandwiches with cream cheese icing 220
Cheat's seafood marinara pizza 116
Cheese & bacon breakfast muffins 58
Citrus jelly cheesecake 208
Crumbed cheese wheels 192
Deconstructed burger bowl 92
Deli-style tuna melts 97
Easy prosciutto-wrapped chicken 128
Freezable egg & bacon muffins 62
Garlic seafood crispbread 'pizzas' 168
Greek salad jar 84
Hash brown stacks with bacon & eggs 70
Lamb bolognese 148
Maple-glazed salmon with watermelon & feta salad 156
Mini cheese & Vegemite scrolls 178
Mushroom crispbread 'pizzas' 169
Nannie's lemon cheesecake 212
Pizza mug muffin 196
Pork lasagne cups 150
Pumpkin & zucchini loaf 94
Roasted vegetable & rice pie 96
Slow-cooked beef cheek lasagne 136
Smoked salmon & cream cheese mug muffin 197
Sweet chilli & cream cheese stuffed dates 187
Cheese & bacon breakfast muffins 58
cheesecakes
Citrus jelly cheesecake 208
Nannie's lemon cheesecake 212
cherries: Rocky road bliss balls 225
chicken
Bang bang chicken salad 76
Chicken & avo pasta salad 80
Chicken & bacon quiches with chickpea crust 82
Chicken & mushroom filo pie 108
Chicken goulash with pasta 138
Chicken sausage rolls 78
Chicken stir-fry with chilli, basil and cashews 152
Chicken, noodle & corn egg drop soup 139
Curried chicken drumsticks with rice 134
Curried chicken patties 145
Deconstructed burger bowl 92
Easy prosciutto-wrapped chicken 128
My go-to chicken curry 122
Paprika chicken nuggets 160
Shake-n-bake chicken on pumpkin smash 146
Sicilian chicken 118
Slow-cooker garlic honey chicken 104
Chicken & avo pasta salad 80
Chicken & bacon quiches with chickpea crust 82
Chicken & mushroom filo pie 108
Chicken goulash with pasta 138
Chicken sausage rolls 78
Chicken stir-fry with chilli, basil and cashews 152
Chicken, noodle & corn egg drop soup 139
chickpeas
Chicken & bacon quiches with chickpea crust 82
Greek salad jar 84
Slow-cooker red lentil & sweet potato curry 154
chillies
Bang bang chicken salad 76
Cheat's seafood marinara pizza 116
Chicken goulash with pasta 138
Chicken stir-fry with chilli, basil and cashews 152
Curried chicken patties 145
Dad's slow-braised beef (trinchado) 130
Maple-glazed salmon with watermelon & feta salad 156
Sichuan sauce 76
Sicilian chicken 118
Spiced coriander & lemon rice 125
Sweet chilli & cream cheese stuffed dates 187
Choc-nut energy bliss bites 172
chocolate
Cheat's mini chocolate 'donuts' 228
Choc-nut energy bliss bites 172
Chocolate-coated pistachio dates 186
Jaffa jelly slice 202
Nannie's lemon cheesecake 212
No-bake chocolate slice 210
Rocky road bliss balls 225
Chocolate-coated pistachio dates 186
Citrus jelly cheesecake 208
coconut
Citrus jelly cheesecake 208
Coconut chia overnight oats 50
Overnight bircher 60
Slow-cooker red lentil & sweet potato curry 154
Sri Lankan-style salmon curry with turmeric rice 110
Coconut chia overnight oats 50
Coffee, oat & date loaf 211
corn
Chicken, noodle & corn egg drop soup 139
Spanish rice 158
Taco-inspired mug muffin 197
Creamy avo sauce 80
crispbread
Garlic seafood crispbread 'pizzas' 168
Mushroom crispbread 'pizzas' 169
Nutty date & banana crispbreads 169
Crumbed cheese wheels 192
cucumbers
Brown rice tuna sushi rolls 100
Chicken & avo pasta salad 80
Greek salad jar 84
Wasabi miso fish bowl 90
Curried chicken drumsticks with rice 134
Curried chicken patties 145
curries
My go-to chicken curry 122
Slow-cooker red lentil & sweet potato curry 154

D

Dad's slow-braised beef (trinchado) 130
dates
Berry flake breakfast bars 55
Blue cheese-stuffed dates 187
Carrot cake sandwiches with cream cheese icing 220
Choc-nut energy bliss bites 172
Chocolate-coated pistachio dates 186
Citrus jelly cheesecake 208
Coconut chia overnight oats 50
Coffee, oat & date loaf 211
High-fibre banana loaves 174
Jaffa jelly slice 202
No-bake chocolate slice 210
Nutty date & banana crispbreads 169
Overnight bircher 60

Rocky road bliss balls 225
Salted 'toffee' fudge balls 222
Sticky date scrolls 180
Sweet chilli & cream cheese stuffed dates 187
Deconstructed burger bowl 92
Deli-style tuna melts 97
'donuts', Cheat's mini chocolate 228

E

Easy apple & gingerbread cake 226
Easy garlic naan 124
Easy oat slice 182
Easy prosciutto-wrapped chicken 128
eggs
Bacon & veggie slice 98
Cauli rice nasi goreng with prawns 114
Chicken & bacon quiches with chickpea crust 82
Chicken, noodle & corn egg drop soup 139
Freezable egg & bacon muffins 62
Hash brown stacks with bacon & eggs 70
Nannie's lemon cheesecake 212
Pumpkin & zucchini loaf 94
Savoury French toast sandwich 68
Slow-cooked beef cheek lasagne 136

F

fish
Wasabi miso fish bowl 90
see also salmon, tuna
Freezable egg & bacon muffins 62
French toast, Savoury, sandwich 68
fried rice, Pork 140
fudge balls, Salted 'toffee' 222

G

Garlic not-butter 123
Garlic seafood crispbread 'pizzas' 168
goulash, Chicken, with pasta 138
Granny's scones 183
Greek lamb meatballs with zoodles 132
Greek salad jar 84
gremolata 111
grocery lists 32–3, 44–5

H

Hash brown stacks with bacon & eggs 70
High-fibre banana loaves 174

J

Jaffa jelly slice 202

L

lamb
Greek lamb meatballs with zoodles 132
Lamb bolognese 148
Lamb bolognese 148
lasagne, Slow-cooked beef cheek 136
lasagne cups, Pork 150
Lemon & thyme pork schnitzels 106
Lemon-glazed tea cakes 214
lemons
60-second lemon mug cake 200
Cheat's seafood marinara pizza 116
Chicken & avo pasta salad 80
Citrus jelly cheesecake 208
dressing 84
Greek lamb meatballs with zoodles 132
Greek salad jar 84
gremolata 111
Lemon & thyme pork schnitzels 106
Lemon-glazed tea cakes 214
Nannie's lemon cheesecake 212
Spiced coriander & lemon rice 125
lentils
Greek lamb meatballs with zoodles 132
Lamb bolognese 148
Slow-cooker red lentil & sweet potato curry 154
tomato sauce 132
Tuscan beef & lentil stew 126
lettuce
Deconstructed burger bowl 92
Greek salad jar 84
limes
Avocado boat prawn cocktails 83
Bang bang chicken salad 76
Citrus jelly cheesecake 208
Maple-glazed salmon with watermelon & feta salad 156
Sichuan sauce 76
Spanish rice 158
Sri Lankan-style salmon curry with turmeric rice 110
loaves
Coffee, oat & date loaf 211
High-fibre banana loaves 174
Pumpkin & zucchini loaf 94
see also bread

M

Mango & passionfruit mug muffin 224
Maple-glazed salmon with watermelon & feta salad 156
meal plans 30–1, 42–3
meal-prepping 12–15, 26–9, 38–41
meatballs, Greek lamb, with zoodles 132
Mince curry & egg pie (Babotie) 129
Mini cheese & Vegemite scrolls 178
muffins
Cheese & bacon breakfast muffins 58
Freezable egg & bacon muffins 62
Mango & passionfruit mug muffin 224
Peanut butter muffins 204
Pizza mug muffin 196
Smoked salmon & cream cheese mug muffin 197
Strawberry cereal breakfast muffins 52
Taco-inspired mug muffin 197
Veggie mug muffin 196
Mum's curried pasta salad 88
Mushroom crispbread 'pizzas' 169
mushrooms
Bacon & veggie slice 98
'Bottom of the fridge' pasta bake 112
Chicken & mushroom filo pie 108
Chicken goulash with pasta 138
Chicken stir-fry with chilli, basil and cashews 152
Curried chicken drumsticks with rice 134
Deconstructed burger bowl 92
Mushroom crispbread 'pizzas' 169
Pork fried rice 140
Slow-cooker garlic honey chicken 104
Spanish rice 158
Stove-top baked beans 54
Veggie mug muffin 196
My go-to chicken curry 122

N

naan, Easy garlic 124
Nannie's lemon cheesecake 212
nasi goreng, Cauli rice, with prawns 114
No-bake chocolate slice 210
No-fuss apple turnover 216
non-starchy vegetables 10
nuggets, Paprika chicken 160
nuts
Avo pancakes 57
Chicken stir-fry with chilli, basil and cashews 152

Choc-nut energy bliss bites 172
Chocolate-coated pistachio dates 186
Coconut chia overnight oats 50
No-bake chocolate slice 210
Nutty date & banana crispbreads 169
Peanut butter muffins 204
Rocky road bliss balls 225
Salted 'toffee' fudge balls 222
Sicilian chicken 118
Nutty date & banana crispbreads 169

O

oats
Citrus jelly cheesecake 208
Coconut chia overnight oats 50
Coffee, oat & date loaf 211
Easy oat slice 182
Jaffa jelly slice 202
Mango & passionfruit mug muffin 224
Overnight bircher 60
Peanut butter muffins 204
Pizza mug muffin 196
Rocky road bliss balls 225
Salted caramel protein overnight oats 66
Strawberry cereal breakfast muffins 52
Taco-inspired mug muffin 197
Veggie mug muffin 196
olives
Dad's slow-braised beef (trinchado) 130
Greek lamb meatballs with zoodles 132
Greek salad jar 84
Maple-glazed salmon with watermelon & feta salad 156
Roasted vegetable & rice pie 96
oranges
Jaffa jelly slice 202
Sweet orange bread 164
osso buco, Slow-cooker 111
Overnight bircher 60
overnight oats, Coconut chia 50
overnight oats, Salted caramel protein 66

P

pancakes
Apple & cinnamon pancakes 56
Avo pancakes 57
Strawberry tray bake pancakes 72
Paprika chicken nuggets 160
passionfruit: Mango & passionfruit mug muffin 224
pasta
'Bottom of the fridge' pasta bake 112
Chicken & avo pasta salad 80
Chicken goulash with pasta 138
Chicken, noodle & corn egg drop soup 139
Lamb bolognese 148
Mum's curried pasta salad 88
Pork lasagne cups 150
Slow-cooked beef cheek lasagne 136
patties
Beef & feta patties 145
Curried chicken patties 145
Quinoa & black bean patties 144
peaches: Mum's curried pasta salad 88
Peanut butter muffins 204
peas
Curried chicken drumsticks with rice 134
Pork fried rice 140
Spanish rice 158
pies
Chicken & mushroom filo pie 108
Mince curry & egg pie (babotie) 129
Roasted vegetable & rice pie 96
pizzas
Cheat's seafood marinara pizza 116
Garlic seafood crispbread 'pizzas' 168
Mushroom crispbread 'pizzas' 169
Pizza mug muffin 196
pork
Easy prosciutto-wrapped chicken 128
Lemon & thyme pork schnitzels 106
Pizza mug muffin 196
Pork fried rice 140
Pork lasagne cups 150
Spanish rice 158
see also bacon
Pork fried rice 140
Pork lasagne cups 150
potatoes
Deconstructed burger bowl 92
Hash brown stacks with bacon & eggs 70
prawns
Avocado boat prawn cocktails 83
Cauli rice nasi goreng with prawns 114
Cheat's seafood marinara pizza 116
Garlic seafood crispbread 'pizzas' 168
Pumpkin & zucchini loaf 94
pumpkins
Hash brown stacks with bacon & eggs 70
Pumpkin & zucchini loaf 94
Roasted vegetable & rice pie 96
Shake-n-bake chicken on pumpkin smash 146

Q

quiches, Chicken & bacon, with chickpea crust 82
Quick veggie pan-fry 64
Quinoa & black bean patties 144

R

Raspberry banana bread 190
Raspberry lattice tart 218
Rebecca's mighty mug muffins 195–7
Rebecca's rock & scrolls 177–80
rice
Brown rice tuna sushi rolls 100
Curried chicken drumsticks with rice 134
Pork fried rice 140
Roasted vegetable & rice pie 96
Spanish rice 158
Spiced coriander & lemon rice 125
Sri Lankan–style salmon curry with turmeric rice 110
Wasabi miso fish bowl 90
Roasted vegetable & rice pie 96
Rocky road bliss balls 225

S

salads
Avocado boat prawn cocktails 83
Bang bang chicken salad 76
Chicken & avo pasta salad 80
Greek salad jar 84
Maple-glazed salmon with watermelon & feta salad 156
Mum's curried pasta salad 88
salmon
Maple-glazed salmon with watermelon & feta salad 156
Smoked salmon & cream cheese mug muffin 197
Sri Lankan–style salmon curry with turmeric rice 110
Salted 'toffee' fudge balls 222
Salted caramel protein overnight oats 66
sandwiches
Carrot cake sandwiches with cream cheese icing 220
Deli-style tuna melts 97
Savoury French toast sandwich 68

sauces
Creamy avo sauce 80
gremolata 111
Sichuan sauce 76
tomato sauce 132
white sauce 136
sausage rolls, Chicken 78
Savoury French toast sandwich 68
schnitzels, Lemon & thyme pork 106
scones, Granny's 183
scrolls
Apple pie scrolls 179
Mini cheese & Vegemite scrolls 178
Sticky date scrolls 180
seafood
Cheat's seafood marinara pizza 116
see also fish, prawns, salmon, tuna
Shake-n-bake chicken on pumpkin smash 146
Sichuan sauce 76
Sicilian chicken 118
slices
Bacon & veggie slice 98
Easy oat slice 182
Jaffa jelly slice 202
No-bake chocolate slice 210
Slow-cooked beef cheek lasagne 136
Slow-cooker garlic honey chicken 104
Slow-cooker osso buco 111
Slow-cooker red lentil & sweet potato curry 154
Smoked salmon & cream cheese mug muffin 197
soup, Chicken, noodle & corn egg drop 139
Spanish rice 158
Spiced coriander & lemon rice 125
spinach
Chicken goulash with pasta 138
Slow-cooker red lentil & sweet potato curry 154
Wasabi miso fish bowl 90
Sri Lankan-style salmon curry with turmeric rice 110
stew, Tuscan beef & lentil 126
Sticky date scrolls 180
stir-fry, Chicken, with chilli, basil and cashews 152
Stove-top baked beans 54
Strawberry cereal breakfast muffins 52
Strawberry flummery 206
Strawberry tray bake pancakes 72
sushi rolls, Brown rice tuna 100
Sweet chilli & cream cheese stuffed dates 187
Sweet orange bread 164
Sweet potatoes
Hash brown stacks with bacon & eggs 70
Slow-cooker red lentil & sweet potato curry 154

T

taco cups, Beef 86
Taco-inspired mug muffin 197
tart, Raspberry lattice 218
tea: Lemon-glazed tea cakes 214
tomatoes
Bang bang chicken salad 76
Beef taco cups 86
'Bottom of the fridge' pasta bake 112
Cheese & bacon breakfast muffins 58
Chicken goulash with pasta 138
Deconstructed burger bowl 92
Greek lamb meatballs with zoodles 132
Greek salad jar 84
Lamb bolognese 148
My go-to chicken curry 122
Pizza mug muffin 196
Quick veggie pan-fry 64
Roasted vegetable & rice pie 96
Sicilian chicken 118
Slow-cooked beef cheek lasagne 136
Slow-cooker osso buco 111
Slow-cooker red lentil & sweet potato curry 154
Spanish rice 158
Sri Lankan-style salmon curry with turmeric rice 110
tomato sauce 132
Tuscan beef & lentil stew 126
Veggie mug muffin 196
Wasabi miso fish bowl 90
tuna
Air-fryer tuna melt bites 188
Brown rice tuna sushi rolls 100
Deli-style tuna melts 97
Garlic seafood crispbread 'pizzas' 168
Mum's curried pasta salad 88
tuna mix 97, 188
turkey: 'Bottom of the fridge' pasta bake 112
turnover, No-fuss apple 216
Tuscan beef & lentil stew 126

V

vegetables
'Bottom of the fridge' pasta bake 112
non-starchy vegetables 10
Roasted vegetable & rice pie 96
Veggie mug muffin 196

W

Wasabi miso fish bowl 90
wasabi miso marinade 90
watermelon: Maple-glazed salmon with watermelon & feta salad 156
watermelon & feta salad 156
Wendy's dates 185–7
Wendy's DIY curry night 120–5
Wendy's favourite snack hack 167–9
Wendy's perfect patties 143–5
white sauce 136
WW
grocery lists 32–3, 44–5
meal plans 30–1, 42–3
meal-prepping 12–15, 26–9, 38–41
personal journey, Rebecca 22–33
personal journey, Wendy 34–45
PersonalPoints 8
what is 6–7

Z

zucchini
Bacon & veggie slice 98
Beef taco cups 86
'Bottom of the fridge' pasta bake 112
Cauli rice nasi goreng with prawns 114
Cheese & bacon breakfast muffins 58
Chicken & bacon quiches with chickpea crust 82
Chicken sausage rolls 78
Chicken stir-fry with chilli, basil and cashews 152
Greek lamb meatballs with zoodles 132
Hash brown stacks with bacon & eggs 70
Lamb bolognese 148
Pork fried rice 140
Pumpkin & zucchini loaf 94
Quick veggie pan-fry 64
Slow-cooker garlic honey chicken 104
Slow-cooker red lentil & sweet potato curry 154
Spanish rice 158
Tuscan beef & lentil stew 126

Pan Macmillan acknowledges the Traditional Custodians of Country throughout Australia and their connections to lands, waters and communities. We pay our respect to Elders past and present and extend that respect to all Aboriginal and Torres Strait Islander peoples today. We honour more than sixty thousand years of storytelling, art and culture.

First published 2022 in Macmillan
by Pan Macmillan Australia Pty Limited
Level 25, 1 Market Street, Sydney, New South Wales
Australia 2000

NATIONAL LIBRARY OF AUSTRALIA
A catalogue record for this book is available from the National Library of Australia

Design by Madeleine Kane
Index by Helena Holmgren
Prop and food styling by Vanessa Austin and Emma Knowles
Food preparation by Sarah Mayoh, Angela Portela and Kerrie Ray
Makeup by Samantha Powell
Colour + reproduction by Splitting Image Colour Studio
Printed in China by Hang Tai Printing Company Limited

Many thanks to the team at WeightWatchers Australia:
Managing Director Mathieu Le Renard
Director – Finance & Commercial Rod Sullivan
Senior Manager Products & Partnerships Trusha Madhoo
Business Manager E-Commerce & Publishing Jade Leung
Food Editor Jane Ash
Food Content & Database Specialist Katherine Christie
Food and Nutrition Data Coordinator Kimberley Pert

10 9 8 7 6 5 4 3 2 1